Successful Preparation For The Psychiatry Oral Exam

HOW TO EFFECTIVELY ORGANIZE YOUR INTERVIEW, ORAL PRESENTATION, AND VIDEO EXAM

Successful Preparation For The Psychiatry Oral Exam

How To Effectively Organize Your Interview, Oral Presentation, And Video Exam

By

Michael G. Rayel, MD

SOAR DIME
Clarenville, NF

Published by:

Soar Dime Limited
PO Box 1834, Clarenville, NF
Canada A0E1J0
Ph: 709-466-5114 or 866-418-7277
Fax: 709-466-2214

Printed in Canada by:
Robinson-Blackmore Printing and Publishing Limited

Canadian Cataloguing in Publication Data

Rayel, Michael G., 1963-
  Successful Preparation for the psychiatry oral exam: how to effectively organize your interview, oral presentation, and video exam

Companion book to the author's Passing Strategies.
Includes bibliographical references and index.
ISBN 0-9687816-3-2

  1. Psychiatry - Examinations. 2. American Board of Psychiatry and Neurology - Examinations. 3. Psychiatry - Examinations - Study guides. 4. Oral Examinations. I. Rayel, Michael G., 1963- . Passing Strategies. II. Title

RC457.R392 2002   616.89"0076   C2001-902601-3

ACKNOWLEDGMENTS

I would like to thank Drs. Thomas Gutheil, Bernard Katz, Justin Schecter, and Bennet Rosner for their review and constructive critique of this book and sound advice. I appreciate the meticulous efforts of my hardworking editors, Mr. Fred Manuel and Mr. Graham Manuel of The Writing Genius.

I would like to express my sincere appreciation and thanks to Dr. Hrair Babikian, the former program director of New York Medical College Psychiatry Residency Program, for giving me my first opportunity to be part of the wonderful world of psychiatry.

I also would like to thank my mother for her inspiring presence. Most of all, I am heartened by my family's enduring support, motivation, encouragement, and understanding during the process of writing the book. To my loving wife Gayzelle, and my wonderful children – Danielle, Joshua, Hannah, and Isaiah, this book is for all of you.

DEDICATION

This book is dedicated to all psychiatry oral exam candidates.

TABLE OF CONTENTS

PART I
ORGANIZE YOUR INTRODUCTION AND INTERVIEW

PART II
ORGANIZE YOUR PRESENTATION

PART III
ORGANIZE YOUR VIDEO EXAM

PART IV
DISORGANIZATION AND OTHER ISSUES

ABOUT THE AUTHOR

Dr. Michael G. Rayel, author of Passing Strategies: A Helpful Guide for the Psychiatry Oral Exam, is a Diplomate of the American Board of Psychiatry and Neurology with Subspecialty Certification in Forensic Psychiatry. He is Certified in Clinical Psychopharmacology by the American Society of Clinical Psychopharmacology. He has received two consecutive Honorable Mention Awards in 1998 and 1999 from the American Academy of Forensic Sciences for his research papers. Dr. Rayel trained in general psychiatry and psychodynamic psychotherapy at New York Medical College, in geriatric psychiatry at New York University Medical Center, and in forensic and correctional psychiatry at Harvard Medical School, Massachusetts Mental Health Center. Dr. Rayel is currently the Director of the Department of Psychiatry at the Dr. G.B. Cross Memorial Hospital, Peninsulas Health Care Corporation located in Newfoundland, Canada.

PREFACE

Disorganization in the interview, oral presentation, and video components of the ABPN Part II examination is a common problem. Psychiatry oral exam candidates have encountered the difficulty and have failed this rigorous test as a result. As a former oral exam candidate, I was once called "disorganized" by my clinical supervisor, but I was never advised on how to deal effectively with disorganization.

Unfortunately, there is a paucity of literature on preparing for this seemingly insurmountable obstacle. Review courses largely fail to recognize and address this important subject. In short, literature and courses do not give specific steps and practical suggestions on organizing properly and minimizing disorganization during the exam.

Successful Preparation for the Psychiatry Oral Exam attempts to fill this void. It is written to help oral exam candidates successfully organize the introduction, interview, oral presentation and video exam phases of the ABPN Part II examination. As such, the book provides detailed how-to techniques for the collection and presentation of data and offers methods to enhance the candidates' performances, thereby improving the chance for success.

Successful Preparation offers several unique features. First, it establishes the essential goals to be achieved during the exam. Secondly, basic and practical techniques to successfully organize the collection and presentation of data are emphasized. Thirdly, the book introduces effective organizing strategies, such as the use of templates, and cassette and video recording, not commonly taught or espoused by review courses, clinical supervisors, and mock reviewers in preparing for the exam. Fourthly, it offers a practical guide for tackling the video component of the exam. Fifthly, the book recognizes the common causes of disorganization, such as anxiety and preoccupation with trifles, and suggests ways to deal with them. And finally, it discusses helpful methodologies in dealing with the intricacies associated with the question-and-answer portion of the exam.

Successful Preparation serves as a companion book to my recently published Passing Strategies: A Helpful Guide for the Psychiatry Oral Exam. Although they differ in approach, style and content, they complement each other. My first book reflected my personal experiences and struggle as a former exam candidate, as well as the experiences of fellow candidates. Successful Preparation offers a more thorough treatment of collecting and presenting data, developing organization strategies, and reckoning with the video exam.

I sincerely hope that this book will assist you as you prepare to face the psychiatry oral exam.

Michael G. Rayel, MD

INTRODUCTION

Organization skills and proficiency in the psychiatric interview and oral presentation are critical for successfully clearing the ABPN hurdle. To approach the oral exam without good organizing skills is to court disaster. Poor organization in the interview can result in unfortunate consequences: failure to get enough data to clinch a diagnosis, failure to focus sufficiently on the important sections of the history, failure to follow clues, and inability to fully assess the patient.

In the same vein, a poor presentation will reflect a candidate's inability to show in a logical, goal-directed fashion the patient's clinical concerns, inability to focus on the real problems afflicting the patient, and inability to describe facts that can support a particular diagnosis. Moreover, a poor presentation may confuse the board examiner and may result in misinterpretation of clinical data. In general, a lack of good organization in both interview and presentation will displease the board examiners leading to an unfavorable assessment of the candidate.

Recently I attended a review course and witnessed a relatively acceptable and organized interview. The presentation, however, was not impressive. An approximate description of what happened is provided below. The candidate presented:

> *The patient is a 35 y/o male who came to treatment due to worry. He reported that there is a strong family history of anxiety. His mother was a worrier and his father was observed to be depressed a lot for no apparent reason. He further said that alcohol problems seemed to run in the family. But the patient stated that he never had any trouble with alcohol or any illicit drug use. Although he admitted having occasional social drinks with friends and co-workers, he denied being in trouble with the law because of drinking.*

The patient said that he was hospitalized in the past because of a bladder problem. He did not mention whether he was experiencing urinary or gallbladder problems. But he reported that the pain associated with it resulted in frequent work absences. His boss eventually fired him. As a result, he became depressed to the point of crying all the time.

Currently, the patient is not depressed but he reports being worried that his wife of five years will abandon him due to financial problems. He said that he was divorced once as a teenager and that it was not an easy situation to handle.

You can perhaps recognize immediately the problem with this presentation. The candidate presented the history with no regard to recognized format as she shifted inappropriately from one section to the next. As shown above, she switched from chief complaint to family history, then to past medical problems. To make matters worse, she subsequently presented personal and social history, then moved to history of present illness, and finally went back to personal and social history. In my opinion, it is not a question of whether the presentation is disorganized. The question is how severely disorganized it is.

Here is another presentation of a colleague after a mock video exam:

This is a case of a 25 y/o female who was diagnosed with schizophrenia several years ago. She reports that she experienced hearing voices as soon as she discovered her husband was actually a gay . . . Pause . . (The candidate looks at his notes for a few seconds.) Pause . . . *She says that she never had a clue as to her husband's sexual orientation until she saw him making love with her male best friend in their bedroom . . .* Pause . . . (The candidate looks at the notes again.) . . . he pauses again . . . (the candidate's eyes appears to scan from one end of the paper to another as if he lost his notes.) *The patient further reports that she was born in the suburbs of California and was raised by her aunt. It was not clear in the history what happened to her parents but I would assume that the parents divorced* . . . Pause . . . (The candidate looks at his notes again.) *She denies any mental illness in the family, although she remembers her brother used to take some kind of nerve pill.*

Returning to the patient's problems, she states that the "voices" told her to divorce her gay husband. She reports that her husband was her high school sweetheart and that there seemed to be no problem then.

In this example, it is evident that the candidate not only demonstrated an inability to put his data in logical order but also engaged in unnecessary pauses resulting in confusion.

It is surprising that despite the significance of organization in the interview and presentation, especially in the board certification examinations, the psychiatric literature contains virtually no information on organizing strategies and competence. Moreover, I cannot remember a curriculum in my residency or even in my fellowship that dealt with this concern. Even psychiatry review courses have no special emphasis on this critical area. During my mock reviews, I was told occasionally that I was disorganized in some areas of the interview and presentation, but I was never taught how to effectively organize.

The importance of organization cannot be overemphasized. Countless numbers of candidates have failed not because they lacked knowledge or because they prepared inadequately. They failed because they did not effectively organize their materials in a way that demonstrated competence and knowledge to the examiners. This book discusses the various techniques for organizing the psychiatry candidate's interview and presentation in the oral examination. If you are not particularly organized, these techniques can help you at least to appear organized before the board examiners during the exam.

Part I of the book deals with organizing your introduction and psychiatric interview. Chapter One discusses the goals to be pursued during the interview. Lacking a goal is comparable to building a house without an architectural plan. It is important to know what must be achieved in order to utilize the thirty-minute period wisely. The goals include establishing rapport, obtaining critical information, and knowing the probable psychiatric diagnosis. Chapter Two addresses the proper approach to introduction. Introducing yourself is only the initial step. You must also thank the interviewee for participating in the exam and outline what is expected in order to minimize uncertainty and surprise.

Chapters Three and Four focus on the core components during the interview. Core components refer to essential elements to be obtained from each section of the history. The budgeting of time is also addressed in this chapter. Chapter Five refers to history-taking techniques such as dealing with difficult and disorganized patients, facilitating a lively and spontaneous interview, and demonstrating empathy with others. In addition, the effective use of mnemonics, outline, checklist, and templates is discussed.

Part II deals with effective organization of your presentation. In Chapter Six, the effective use of chronology, transitional statements and pronouncements is discussed. Chapter Seven discusses how mnemonics, outline, checklist, and templates are helpful in organizing the presentation of the case. Techniques to improve your discussion of case formulation, differential diagnosis, and treatment plan are dealt with in Chapter Eight. Finally, the importance of rigorous practice for this examination cannot be overemphasized. Engaging in mock examinations and reading texts are of course necessary in preparing for this challenging test. But you must also practice by using video and cassette recordings of your interview and presentation, followed by analysis of your performance. This aspect is discussed in Chapter Nine.

Part III deals with organizing the video exam. Chapter Ten discusses the importance of using the Stop, look and listen technique. The video interview requires keen perception since you are attempting to discern any pathology while listening carefully to gain vital information. In addition to these tasks, you must take pertinent notes that will help in recording and retrieving data during the presentation. Note-taking is addressed in Chapter Eleven.

Part IV discusses the various factors leading to disorganization during the psychiatry oral exam. Strategies to address this issue are explored in Chapter Twelve. The last chapter deals with effective organizing techniques involved in the question-and-answer portion of the ABPN exam.

PART 1

ORGANIZE YOUR INTRODUCTION AND INTERVIEW

First impressions last. My clinical supervisor once told me that a remarkable introduction and psychiatric interview by an oral exam candidate helps gain the favor of the board examiners. Before you plunge into the fire, know what you want to achieve. You need a goal. It is also vital to know the core components to be included in the introduction and history. The next few chapters will assist you in establishing an impressive first salvo, thereby leaving the board examiner with the imprint of a competent psychiatrist deserving a diplomate status.

 CHAPTER 1

Have These Goals In Mind

Doing an interview without a goal is like cooking without knowing the recipe, or like building a house without an architectural plan. Disorganization is inevitable in an interview without the objective in mind. Similarly, a candidate who approaches the exam without methodical preparation will likely fail. One candidate I encountered in a board review course asked the patient questions at random. He jumped from one section to another, starting from the personal and social history, to HPI, to family history, then to PMH and finally back to HPI. He not only confused the mock examiner but also effortlessly perplexed the patient and the audience. As far as I am concerned, you are not entitled to manifest your formal thought disorder while conducting an interview, especially during an exam.

This is why having clear goals is of cardinal importance in passing the exam. Strive to: 1) establish a rapport or alliance with the patient, 2) determine the probable psychiatric illness or diagnosis, 3) acquire information about issues or concerns that need to be addressed in treatment, 4) know the appropriate treatment plan, 5) know whether a patient is safe or not, 6) know basic or core components in each section well, 7) get enough information within a thirty-minute period and allocate appropriate time for each section, and 8) establish an alliance with the board examiner.

ESTABLISH RAPPORT OR ALLIANCE WITH THE PATIENT

The cooperation of the patient can make or break your chances of passing the exam. An inability to form an alliance with the patient will interfere with the unveiling of information. Weak rapport usually results in one-word responses to your questions, poor eye contact, and a lack of enthusiasm to "help out." Worse still, the patient might disrupt the whole process by prematurely terminating the interview and deciding not to participate at all, leaving you with little or no information.

Establish rapport immediately – during the first few seconds of contact. A few simple techniques are useful. A warm handshake coupled with a genuine smile can go a long way. Allowing the patient a few seconds of "free talk" about the traffic or weather helps break the ice. I emphasize a few seconds since you cannot afford more than this. Similarly, guiding the patient to a seat or hanging his or her jacket shows respect. Telling the patient what to expect, such as the duration of the exam and explaining the need to obtain personal information, can simplify the whole process and perhaps dispel the mystery of the exam. Asking broad, open-ended questions can make a guarded patient more responsive.

Forming an alliance does not stop after the introduction phase but rather continues throughout the interview process. Even in the closing phase, convey common courtesies sincerely such as thank you and goodbye to maintain the alliance you have created earlier. As a candidate of the oral exam, make an effort to create the context for a successful interview while maintaining rapport with the patient throughout the exam. You are encouraged to come up with your own techniques, by reflecting on your clinical experience.

4

DETERMINE THE PROBABLE PSYCHIATRIC ILLNESS OR DIAGNOSIS

Since knowing the type of illness the patient is suffering from is a basic requirement of this exam, the ability to gather information to establish a diagnosis is central. Appropriate questions focus on the patient's predominant problem that led to a visit to a mental health clinic or hospital. Knowledge of the DSM-IV criteria is very helpful in this regard. Know the type, duration and chronology of symptoms. The presence or absence of stressors that could have precipitated or aggravated the psychological problems must be determined. Moreover, you need to know the consequences of the symptoms for the person's life, such as impairment in social, marital, and occupational functioning.

Questions should also focus on the circumstances relevant to whether the patient has sought help as a result of the psychological symptoms and impairment in functioning. If treatment was not sought, you have to probe for a reason. Is the patient in denial or suffering from poor insight? Does the patient belong to an ethnic group that strongly opposes or stigmatizes mental health workers or rejects psychiatric diagnosis and its intervention? Is there a family history of the patient's concerns? Does the patient have a prior history of the symptoms? Consider pertinent negatives during interview. Learn not only what symptoms or stressors are present but also *what is not present*. If a patient, for instance, has suffered from depression, ask about the presence of "high periods" in the past. If a patient has suffered from paranoia, you may want to ask about the presence of hallucinations or bizarre delusions. Establishing the presence or absence of symptoms can help in making the appropriate diagnosis.

In addition, look for particular signs during the interview and MSE that could give a clue to appropriate diagnosis. For example, psychomotor retardation in a patient complaining of anxiety symptoms may indicate clinical depression rather than anxiety disorder. The presence of bizarre behavior, poor personal hygiene, and guarded stance during interview may point to the possibility of psychotic disorder. A surgical neck scar, indicative of a previous thyroidectomy, on a depressed patient may point to hypothyroidism as the cause of the symptom. Probe for necessary information – from history (HPI, past psychiatric history, etc.) to MSE – that help you formulate the psychiatric diagnosis.

ACQUIRE RELEVANT ISSUES THAT NEED TO BE ADDRESSED IN TREATMENT

Knowing the DSM diagnosis alone is insufficient because you are conceptualizing the patient in terms of an abstract body of symptoms. For a more complete picture, address the personal, marital, occupational, or familial issues that could have precipitated or aggravated the patient's mental illness. Did the patient's prior sexual abuse result in current mood swings and self-destructive behavior? Has a current, failed relationship caused the emotional difficulties? Or did the psychological problems precede the marital conflict? Furthermore, try to understand the patient's lifestyle and unique world-view. The 30-minute time constraint may prevent you from gaining a fairly exhaustive knowledge of the patient. But you strive to understand the person rather than focus only on a set of symptoms.

KNOW THE APPROPRIATE TREATMENT PLAN

After gathering the necessary information such as the predominant signs and symptoms, pertinent personal issues, significant familial history, remarkable medical problem, and so on, determine the appropriate treatment plan. Follow the basic dictum that the treatment plan conforms to the patient's specific and unique problems. A "shotgun" diagnosis and treatment plan will neither help you treat patients nor help you pass the exam. Putting all depressed patients in a "box" with the same treatment intervention, such as giving Prozac and providing psychodynamic psychotherapy, may not be seen favorably by the examiners. Ordering excessive laboratory exams or making a referral to a specialist simply because it is the "politically correct" thing to do will not help either. The treatment plan addresses not only the unique problems of the patient, but also the relevance and efficacy of the intervention, the expense, the ease of administration, the side effect profile, the risks and benefits, and so on. There should always be a strong rationale for choosing a particular treatment intervention.

KNOW PATIENT'S SAFETY

Recognize during the interview whether the patient is a threat to self or others. There are two reasons for this. First, it is good clinical practice to keep patients safe. It is important to determine patients' ability to keep themselves safe because the intervention may vary according to their clinical status. The approach to a patient who has already attempted suicide is different from the approach to a patient who is just contemplating it. A suicidal patient with supportive family members may be seen in the outpatient clinic as opposed to a patient with a chaotic family background and hypercritical spouse. Moreover, a patient who impulsively threatens to hurt a neighbor after a car accident may require a different approach from a patient who has meticulously planned the demise of a philandering husband. Secondly, keeping your patient safe and determining the level of safety demonstrate to the board examiners that you are a "safe" and reliable clinician, and that you deserve to belong to the group of qualified and board certified specialists. Any hint of recklessness in handling a patient may give examiners sufficient ground to give you an unsatisfactory mark.

In the board exam, you have to demonstrate before the examiners a significant degree of competence in dealing with a patient manifesting an acute suicidal or homicidal risk. Recognizing the presence of risk is necessary but what you do after is more significant. Obtaining detailed information about the ideation, plan, or trigger mechanisms is appropriate. However, you must demonstrate your readiness and urgency to keep patient and others safe. For a patient who is an acute suicidal risk, for instance, you need to inform the hospital, ward, or clinic staffs about such risk immediately after the interview.

KNOW THE BASIC OR CORE COMPONENTS IN EACH SECTION WELL

Each section of the interview and presentation contains basic must-know components. The introduction, history of present illness, past psychiatric history, mental state examination, and so on should contain the necessary ingredients to make these sections as complete as possible. The absence of these core components will likely lead to failure in the oral examination. Focus your energies, concentration, and time on these components and make appropriate use of the thirty-minute period.

OBTAIN ENOUGH INFORMATION WITHIN THE THIRTY-MINUTE PERIOD

Exceeding the designated period for evaluation happens frequently and seems acceptable in much clinical practice. However in the examination, be aware of the limited time allowed to obtain necessary information to clinch the appropriate diagnosis, to recognize the appropriate treatment plan, to understand the real concerns and problems of the patient, and to establish rapport. Rapport is again emphasized because information, correct diagnosis, and treatment plan in themselves will not guarantee success.

The interview should be done in thirty minutes. Allocate appropriate time for each section of the history. There are many ways of allotting the time. In my previous book Passing Strategies, I suggested that you divide your interview into three sections. The first fifteen minutes are devoted to introduction, chief complaint, history of present illness and past psychiatric history. The introduction can be done in less than one minute. The next ten minutes are devoted to past medical history, family history, and personal and social history. The last five minutes are devoted to the formal mental status examination. This strategy will reduce frequent glancing at your watch, thus allowing more eye contact with the patient and thereby showing the patient that you are interested, that you care.

ESTABLISH AN ALLIANCE WITH THE BOARD EXAMINER

Most colleagues, mock examiners, and board review courses have espoused the need to establish an alliance with the patient. This is understandable given that the focus of the exam is a proper psychiatric interview whose purpose is the acquisition of significant information to be presented to the examiner. However, there is minimal discussion about the need to make an alliance with the board examiner. In a sense, making an alliance with the examiner is just as important as making an alliance with the patient. Examiners have the power to pass you and praise you. If they fail you, the goal of joining an "elite" group of psychiatrists will remain elusive.

Making an alliance with a board examiner is not about engaging in casual conversation before the exam, making jokes, or offering dinner invitations. Making an alliance simply involves showing the examiners respect by demonstrating appropriate gestures. Be tactful, diplomatic, open and sincere. Avoid unnecessary argument when the board examiners explore the extent of your knowledge. Do not ignore the clues offered by them and do not disregard their remarks about your diagnosis and treatment plan. Avoid any form of animosity because you know exactly who will fail if you do. Making an alliance begins with giving an honest greeting or a warm handshake. It is wearing a professional attire appropriate for this special encounter. It also involves showing utmost respect to the patient.

Demonstrating that you have the humility to listen to the opinions of others and the courage to confront a constant barrage of questions will be seen in a positive light.

TIPS

- **Establish a rapport with the patient right from the outset and throughout the interview process.**

- **Determine the probable psychiatric illness resulting in functional impairment.**

- **Know the stressors and aggravating factors to be addressed in treatment.**

- **Base the treatment plan on the patient's unique and specific disabling symptoms.**

- **Know whether a patient is a threat to self or others.**

- **Focus your energy and time on the core components in each section.**

- **Obtain enough information and allot appropriate time to each section.**

- **Show board examiners utmost respect.**

CHAPTER 2

Start With A Winning Introduction

In the introduction section, take basic steps to establish rapport and to show respect to the patient. Here, the patient's (and examiners') first impressions of you occur. A bad impression, arising from a perceived disrespect, may create a reluctance to "help" the examinee. Patients, who may have had bad experiences with prior physicians, health care workers, or authority figures such as parents or close relatives, will interpret unfavorably any unnecessary gestures or condescending styles of speech. Try your best to be nice during the examination.

I suggest that in the introduction phase you spend just enough time to tell the patient the purpose of the interview and examination, to start an alliance, and to ask for basic information. Thirty to sixty seconds is sufficient.

The core components in the introduction section include: a) introducing yourself, b) thanking patients for their participation, c) inquiring about demographics, d) determining inpatient and outpatient status, and e) telling patients what to expect.

INTRODUCE YOURSELF

Introducing yourself to the patient, in the examination or in your clinic, is a good practice. A patient feels comfortable disclosing information to someone who is not a complete stranger. Giving your name and your status is a good start in establishing a "connection," and this gesture shows respect. Introduction is simple and straightforward.

Example:
> Hi! I'm Dr. Johnson. As you probably already know, I'm a psychiatrist who needs to take this oral examination to become board certified.

Request the patient's name and ask how he or she wishes to be addressed. Some patients prefer to be called just by their first names, as opposed to the formal Mr. or Mrs. title.

Example:
> May I know your name?
>
> *Sure. I'm Susan F.*
>
> How do you want me to call you during this interview?
>
> *Susan is fine.*
>
> Ok then.

THANK PATIENTS FOR THEIR PARTICIPATION

Some patients already know the purpose of the examination, and having participated in the process before, they are fully aware that you will be "grilled" by the examiners. They may also know that they will be asked the same questions asked of them previously. It is difficult for some patients to participate in this process, especially answering the same questions repeatedly and revisiting personal issues again and again. Despite their good intentions, the pain and sorrow associated with their past may re-emerge. Show them respect by thanking them for their participation.

Example:
> Well Susan, thank you so much for participating in this process of examining my qualifications as a psychiatrist.

You're welcome.

INQUIRE ABOUT DEMOGRAPHICS

Inquire about three main demographic factors – age, marital status, and occupational status. Various types of mental illness are common to a particular age group. For instance, the onset of schizophrenia frequently occurs in the late teens or early twenties. Age is also an important consideration particularly in prescribing medication. The dosage of a drug for a 75 year old patient will be about a half or a third of the regular adult dose. Secondly, marital status reveals important aspects of a patient's risks and available support system. For example, an elderly widower may represent a higher risk to commit suicide than a 50 y/o married man. Inquiry into marital status may also disclose the presence of certain stressors, such as an extramarital affair by the patient's spouse, impending divorce, financial problems incurred in sending the children to school, or mortgage problems. Thirdly, occupational status may indicate the patient's level of functioning and the type of stressors being experienced.

Example:
> Before I proceed with my interview, I want to know some important information about you. How old are you?

I'm forty-five.

Ok. Are you married or single?

I'm a single mother.

I see. How do you support your family?

I work two jobs. In the morning, I work as a secretary. This is my regular job. Two evenings a week I work as a waitress at a local bar.

That sounds quite demanding!

DETERMINE INPATIENT OR OUTPATIENT STATUS

Ask questions to determine the patient's clinical status, i.e. outpatient or inpatient, which may indicate the severity of the patient's illness. The patient's clinical status may also reveal the onset of the illness, the coping ability of the patient, and the extent to which the patient's functioning has been impaired by the illness. It also provides information about the level of support the patient has in the family and community. Patients with severe mental illness usually end up in hospital if they lack support from their families, if they have no adequate coping skills, if their illnesses prevent them from performing the activities of daily life, and if they are a threat to themselves or others.

Example:
  Susan, are you currently receiving treatment as an outpatient or inpatient?

  Dr. X is seeing me as an outpatient.

  I see.

TELL PATIENTS WHAT TO EXPECT

Some patients may not know exactly what will transpire in the examination or what the process entails. Some may think that the interview is important for their treatment. Clarify for the patient your limited role and state that any issues regarding treatment should be addressed to his or her regular psychiatrist. In this way, you show respect to both the patient and to the patient's regular doctor. Your integrity in the eyes of the interviewee and board examiner may be enhanced by this simple reminder.

A central part of telling the patient what to expect consists of "priming" the individual about the possibility of digging up painful past issues, a frequently difficult process. Unusual surprises that could cause alarm to the patient have to be prevented or minimized.

Example:

> In this thirty-minute interview, I will ask you questions regarding your concerns, symptoms, and problems that prompted you to seek mental health services. Later, I will ask you for some details about your past, about your current and past health problems, and about your personal and family history.

> *I see.*

Telling patients what to expect may be helpful in making effective transitions later in the interview.

Example:

> *Things have been tough. My husband lost his job. Then my boss made complaints against me. I don't know what's gonna happen next. I just can't deal with this anymore.*

> You sound upset and worried about the whole thing. What you're going through is certainly stressful **..** (pause)**. .**

Have you ever wondered whether life is not worth living anymore?

I was thinking about that. It's been difficult, you know.

Have you thought about hurting yourself?

Never. Nothing like that. I don't think I can do anything like that.

I see . . . (pause). . A short while ago, I mentioned I was going to ask you about your family. Tell me, has there been any mental illness in your family?

TIPS

- Introduce yourself to the patient.

- Show respect to patients by thanking them for their participation.

- Inquire about demographics such as age, marital and occupational status.

- Ascertain the patient's status, whether inpatient or outpatient, as it may indicate the severity of the illness and the patient's coping abilities.

- Tell patients what will transpire in the examination to minimize unusual surprises.

CHAPTER 3

Obtain An Adequate History I

T he importance of a clinical history cannot be overemphasized. Without it, you cannot understand the problems and concerns of the patient and you cannot arrive at a diagnosis and treatment plan. I remember one of my professors in medical school scolding my classmate, who was more preoccupied with her personal appearance than with taking a lengthy medical history of her patient, and directing her to take off her white coat. He remarked, "You don't deserve a white coat if you can't get a proper history . . . Your white coat and stethoscope can't treat a patient." After that episode, she began to spend more time on obtaining a detailed history than on improving her appearance.

To obtain an adequate history, aim to 1) focus on the core components in each section of the history, 2) budget your time, and 3) begin the mental status examination (MSE) prior to the formal MSE.

FOCUS ON THE CORE COMPONENTS IN EACH SECTION

Each section of the history has core components, must-know information to be obtained during the interview and to be reported during the presentation of the case. These core components are fundamental ingredients requiring completeness if you wish to avoid exam failure. It is hard to picture, for instance, a history of present illness or HPI with exhaustive narration of symptoms but with no information on the precipitants and no account of the dysfunction caused by those symptoms. Likewise, a past psychiatric history or PPH with information on psychiatric disorder and suicidal behavior, but which has failed to address the treatment intervention received or prior violent tendencies, is unacceptable to most clinicians, especially the board examiners. Understanding the importance of these core components and describing them thoroughly should be the focus of interview and presentation.

History of Present Illness

The core components of history of present illness (HPI) include: a) symptomatology, b) stressors, c) chronology of symptoms and events, d) consequences of the problem, e) treatment received, f) pertinent negatives, and g) suicidality or homicidality.

Symptomatology

This component is the bread and butter of any interview and presentation. Just knowing a combination of symptoms is not enough. Rather, it is crucial to recognize the predominant symptom or the major concern that prompted the patient's referral to a mental health professional. How do you know that the symptom the patient complains about is the predominant one? How will you know which predominant symptom to pursue? There are four practical techniques that help determine the patient's predominant problem. First, focus on the patient's chief complaint, since it represents the window, in most cases, to the patient's emotional or clinical state. If a patient gives depression as the reason for seeking treatment, it is more likely that he or she is suffering from a depressive disorder rather than a psychotic or anxiety disorder. Since people define certain words differently, it is necessary to know the exact complaint by getting the patient to define or describe the symptoms, such as manic, anxious, confused, depressed, "nerve problems" more explicitly. If the patient, for example, complains of "anxiety," ask for the individual's experience in detail. Is the patient actually referring to panic attacks, excessive worry, or depression?

Secondly, determine the most distressing or disabling problem that the patient suffers from. A patient who initially complains of depression may actually suffer from chronic bizarre delusions and disturbing hallucinations. Some patients, who may have two to three co-morbid psychiatric disorders, should be asked about the symptom that warrants treatment priority. Thirdly, consider the patient's striking appearance or clinical presentation. A patient who frequently mumbles and manifests bizarre posture may actually suffer from a primary psychosis despite complaints of depression. In the same vein, a patient reporting anxiety may actually suffer predominantly from a clinical depression after the individual exhibits tearfulness and severe psychomotor retardation. And fourthly, you can focus on the symptom that the patient prefers to emphasize. In that way you gain a lot of free information without much prompting.

After establishing the predominant symptom or problem, attempt to obtain detailed information. Ask about the associated signs and symptoms in order to form a reasonable differential diagnosis using the DSM IV criteria. In a case of depression, ask about the presence of neurovegetative signs and symptoms such as the impairment of energy, libido, appetite, concentration, and sleep. Also pursue associated functional impairment and related distress (American Psychiatric Association, 1994).

Patients may have more than one predominant symptom. For example, a patient experiencing depression may also complain about severe panic attacks. Here your goal is to establish whether the predominant symptoms are separate diagnostic entities or whether they are actually manifestations of only one psychiatric disorder. In this case, you might consider the possibility of a major depressive disorder co-morbid with panic disorder. Using DSM IV criteria, you need to probe associated symptoms of panic attacks, such as unexpected occurrence of palpitations, breathing difficulty, and inappropriate worry about having future panic attacks, and of clinical depression, such as thoughts of death and feelings of guilt or worthlessness (American Psychiatric Association, 1994).

When a patient presents with two or three predominant symptoms, a potential dilemma arises if you do not know which symptom deserves the main focus during the examination or interview. For example, a patient may complain about severe depression, serious anxiety, and nightmares and, based on initial information, all of these problems may actually represent distinct diagnostic entities. In clinical practice, you can explore individual predominant symptoms in detail because you have ample time. However, in the oral examination with its thirty-minute constraint, you may be able to focus on only one disabling symptom and then try to establish a diagnosis based on the DSM IV criteria. For instance, if the patient's chief complaint is depression, the next step is to ask for associated signs and symptoms, impairment in functioning, and associated severe distress. You need not explore all symptoms present in the interviewee. Instead, you ask for enough symptoms to clinch one DSM IV diagnosis.

Example:

Tell me Susan. What brought you to treatment?

I'm having a tough time . . . It's been very difficult lately. It seems that everyday I have to push myself to get up or do anything. I just want to lie down in bed and hope that nobody would call and bother me. I just don't know why.

How long have you been like this?

It's been a while now. I don't know when it actually started. I just noticed that it's been more of a struggle lately.

How do you mean?

I don't have any energy. Perhaps it's because I just toss and turn at night. I just can't sleep. At work, I can't focus on what I do. My boss has mentioned to me that I've missed a lot of details in the document I prepared. I'm afraid I'm gonna lose my job . . . (crying)

You sound really bothered by the whole thing. Tell me how you've been feeling lately.

Lousy! Down in the dumps. I don't know why I've been feeling like this. I cry for no reason. I've been very irritable. My co-workers have noticed that I easily fly off the handle. In the morning, I just want to cry, hoping that God would just allow me to die . . . (crying again)

Have you seen a mental health worker or psychiatrist?

My friend advised me to see a psychiatrist. I went last week. He seemed to be nice. He put me on an anti-depressant. So far, I haven't seen any change.

Is it appropriate to pursue in detail the other predominant symptoms? The answer is yes and no. Yes, you may pursue them if you still have time left in the interview. No, if there is no more time left to pursue the other disabling symptoms in detail. But you should mention the possibility of another disorder in your presentation or discussion of the differential diagnosis. Mention during presentation that you could have pursued those possibilities if you had more time. But, as stated above, given the thirty-minute limit you will likely have to focus only on the number of symptoms necessary to clinch a diagnosis.

Stressors

Determine the precipitant of any psychological symptoms so that it can be addressed in treatment. In other words, you have to identify the stressor that prompted the patient to seek treatment or hospitalization. For example, a patient who has just broken up with a spouse may need crisis intervention. If that patient has been physically and sexually abused by the husband and has been receiving death threats, she may need intervention by the authorities and the comfort and safety of a women's shelter. Knowing the aggravating factors such as unsupportive and critical spouse, financial concerns, and lack of housing is also critical in helping the patient in a holistic manner. A patient who just lost a house and a job may need the support of social services. The scope of a treatment plan varies with the type of stressors involved.

Example:

What has been going on in your life lately that has made you feel depressed?

I don't know the exact reason why I feel down. But since my boyfriend of ten years went to prison for a drug charge, I've noticed that I'm not the same anymore.

Tell me what happened to your boyfriend?

Well, we've been living together happily for a while. One day, he met this guy who offered him dope. He didn't like it at first. But soon, he became involved with it. Everything went downhill for him since then. He began using crack, then heroin. He didn't have that much money, so he began to sell drugs. Eventually his activities caught up with him. Cops came one day to arrest him.

Listening to the patient's narration of all these concerns is beneficial in itself. It enhances rapport since you show interest and concern.

Knowing when the stressor happened and assessing its severity and consequences are decisive in knowing the type of diagnosis or difficulty a patient may be suffering from. A patient who, as a child, had been threatened and forced to have sex by a relative, may have experienced nightmares and flashbacks for many years. In the interview, moreover, it may be necessary to tie the stressor to the occurrence of the psychological symptoms. For example, ask the patient, "As a result of the molestation, can you tell me what has happened to you emotionally?"

Chronology of symptoms and events

Establish the chronology of events by asking the patient for certain highlights related to the emotional problem, such as the occurrence of precipitating stressors, the onset of symptoms, the worsening of the conditioning, the time treatment was sought, occurrence of disability, and events prior to the hospitalization. Knowing these highlights helps you organize clearly the whole story when you present the case later.

Example:
That's too bad. So when was he arrested?

A year ago. But he got convicted only six months ago. It's been tough since then. I'm not used to being alone, you know.

When did you start to feel down?

It's been a while. Perhaps, about two or three months ago. When things got worse lately, my colleague advised me to see a psychiatrist. So I went last week.

Consequences of the problem

Here, you need to establish the effects of the emotional difficulty. Did the patient experience severe distress or impairment in functioning? Did the patient lose a job due to the psychological symptoms? Did he or she become violent? In essence, you consider personal and marital conflicts, problems on the job or in the community, financial concerns, inability to function and to take care of oneself, severe distress, threats to self or others, and any problems that arise from the emotional difficulty.

Example:

As a result of your depression, have you experienced any problems with your functioning?

As I mentioned before, I can't focus at work. I've made errors lately that angered my boss. Also, I have to push myself every morning. I don't have any energy so I haven't cleaned my house. It's very messy now. I'm not like this.

Treatment received

During the interview, ask whether treatment was sought as a result of the psychological problems. If treatment was sought, when did it happen? Did the patient have the initiative to seek the needed treatment? If treatment was not sought, why? Questions that probe the reason for seeking or not seeking treatment reveal the patient's level of motivation for treatment and insight about the illness. They may also illuminate the kind of concerns and support the patient enjoys from family members. Generally, knowing the type of treatment received guides you in choosing the appropriate medication dosage and regimen. Certainly, you would not recommend the same dose and medications that have previously failed to help the patient.

Example:

> You mentioned a while ago that you were seen by a psychiatrist.

> *Yeah. He put me on a small dose of antidepressant. I've been taking the pill for a week. So far, I haven't noticed any difference. I'm not well.*

> I see. Is this your first time being put on medication?

> *It was recommended before but I hate pills. I never took it. Yeah. This is my first time to try pills.*

> What made you hate pills before?

> *I just felt that people would laugh at me taking "nerve pills." It's also a sign of weakness to take pills. I don't know why I think like this.*

Pertinent negatives

Pertinent negatives are helpful in the differential diagnosis. For instance, a present and past history of depression without prior history of mania generally rules out the possibility of bipolar disorder. Likewise, the absence of hallucinations in a patient with paranoid delusions may decrease the likelihood of schizophrenia as the diagnosis. A patient may constantly complain of depression but the absence of neurovegetative signs and symptoms may rule out major depression. Board examiners will think that you know your psychiatry well if you ask relevant questions to rule in or rule out an illness.

Example:

> Susan, some people who feel depressed say they also experience something unusual or new to them like hearing voices that are not there or feeling suspicious that people are out to get them. Have you ever experienced hearing voices?

No. I'm not that bad.

How about feeling suspicious that people are out to get you?

Nothing like that. Occasionally though, I feel that my co-workers are talking about me. I'm not bothered by it though.

Have you experienced the feeling opposite to being depressed? I mean, do you feel really happy, more happy than usual, as if you're under the influence of drugs?

I've never felt really happy in my life. I've been depressed all my life, I guess.

Suicidality or homicidality

It is always good clinical practice to determine a patient's safety level, especially in the light of severe mental illness such as major depression or paranoia accompanied by command auditory hallucinations. Doing a suicidal and homicidal risk assessment routinely in your clinic is central in keeping the patient safe and in knowing a patient's diagnosis, treatment plan, and prognosis. For example, a patient with a long history of causing superficial laceration in her forearm and who has made several attempts to swallow razor blades may demonstrate borderline traits indicating an option of short-term as opposed to long-term hospitalization. Someone who has made multiple threats and attempts to overdose in front of a departing wife in broad daylight may just need outpatient counseling, and the prognosis may not be necessarily poor. On the other hand, hospitalization may be indicated for a patient who seriously planned his own death several weeks ago by hanging, and who made an attempt while everyone was away.

Failure to ask questions which probe for the presence of suicidal or homicidal thoughts shows an inadequate interview. Violent behaviour or homicidal thoughts in the context of mood instability or command auditory hallucination should be taken seriously and assessed properly. Obtain a detailed assessment of risk. Ask about the presence and frequency of ideation or gesture. For those with ideation, check for suicidal or homicidal intent. Ask for the details of the plan. How is the patient going to do it – by way of hanging, stabbing, cutting the wrist, using a gun? Does he have access to a weapon? When is he going to do it? Does he intend to leave a suicide note? Has he distributed his possessions to relatives? Ask for reasons why he would do it and what he would like to accomplish.

During the length of the interview, you have to probe for the presence of risk factors in the patient and family such as history of poor impulse control, ongoing crisis, co-morbid mental illness, medical problems or substance abuse/dependence, prior significant suicidal or homicidal ideations and attempts.

Example:

You mentioned a while ago that sometimes you hope that God would allow you to die. Tell me about that.

That's what I feel. I just want to sleep and never wake up. Life does not mean anything to me. I think I've lived long enough. I'm ready to face my creator.

Have you ever thought of ending your life?

Sometimes. I just don't know what it would be like to die. I think it's peaceful.

What plans have you had lately to end your life?

I initially thought of using a gun. But I figured it would be too messy. Perhaps by hanging. But I don't want to break my neck. To be honest with you, I don't know what to do.

Is it possible that you don't really want to end your life?

Possibly. If I wanted to do it, I could have done it a long time ago. But because I have kids, I don't know what would happen to them when I'm gone.

So your kids stop you from hurting yourself?

You can say that.

Doing suicidal, homicidal, and violence assessment in the examination illustrates to the examiner your utmost concern toward the patient.

Interviewing a **clinically stable patient with a psychiatric history** presents a challenge. As clinicians, we are used to seeing acutely sick patients during the first visit and interview. However, during the examination, it is not unusual to interview a clinically stable and asymptomatic patient but one who has a clear psychiatric history. In a way, it is helpful to have a willing, stable, and cooperative patient. On the other hand, some patients who are still acutely ill may not agree to the hassle of repetitive questioning by clinicians. As you well know, some of those seen at a university hospital may have already been interviewed several times by trainees such as medical, psychology, and social work students, residents, nursing staffs, fellows, and then finally by attending physicians. At times, acutely ill patients may still present signs and symptoms such as irritability, severe psychomotor retardation or agitation, and disorganized behavior that make them impossible to interview.

Clinically stable and asymptomatic patients, however, present a peculiar dilemma for board examinees. Some of them have wondered how to obtain a history of present illness or HPI from a patient who has been stable, since technically there is no present illness or symptoms. Most challenging are those patients who have been stable and asymptomatic for many years. Examinees are confused as to what questions to ask, whether to start with the past or present, and what information to obtain about the current state.

I recommend that in this situation you should look at the whole landscape of the patient's illness. Obtain the **history of mental illness** rather than simply a history of present illness. You may start with the prior episode or episodes and get as much information as possible about the stressors, symptoms, treatment and so on. For patients with multiple episodes, complicated psychiatric treatment and numerous hospitalizations, begin with the most recent episode or hospitalization. Once significant information is obtained for understanding the patient's psychiatric condition, proceed to probe into *current* clinical status, treatment, and functioning.

For clinically stable and asymptomatic patients but with a psychiatric history, core components include: a) description of the events that resulted in psychiatric treatment, b) subsequent events after the psychiatric episode, c) current functioning, treatment, and clinical status and d) suicidality or homicidality.

History of Mental illness

Description of the events that resulted in psychiatric treatment

Information you should obtain about the prior episode includes signs and symptoms, precipitating and aggravating stressors, diagnosis, treatment received, chronology, suicidality or homicidality, and pertinent negatives.

Subsequent events after the psychiatric episode

After the episode, you may need to ask about the persistent symptoms. Some patients who are mentally ill, such as those with psychotic disorder, may still complain of occasional and yet persistent auditory hallucination and paranoia despite optimum treatment. Treatment received – whether it has helped or not – should be known since it will help you make the appropriate treatment recommendations later in the exam. Treatment changes such as increase or decrease in the dose given in response to a patient's concerns, including side effects and lack of efficacy, must be noted. Also ascertain the patient's placement or residence, employment, stressors and challenges, coping mechanisms, functioning, daily activities, and support from the community and family.

Example:

How did you do after the last episode of depression?

I did well at first. I was discharged to an apartment in a small community. I attended the treatment program religiously and was seeing a mental health worker to help me learn how to cope with things. Soon the pressure of everyday life started to get to me.

How do you mean?

I realized that it was not as easy as I thought. I soon developed depression again. I could hardly sleep and had to force myself to attend the programs.

Did you get any help?

Well yeah. The psychiatrist put me on another drug in addition to Celexa. I think it was Trazodone. It helped me sleep and I felt calm when I took it. He also referred me to group therapy.

Did the combination of medications help you?

Eventually I began to feel better. After a few weeks, I started to do walking exercises again.

Current functioning, treatment, and clinical status

This section may include reference to daily activities and hobbies. Is the patient very active physically? Does he enjoy any of his hobbies? Determine in detail the patient's current employment status and motivation to keep a job. If he is not employed, is there any attempt to find a job? Is the patient emotionally stable enough to plan or start a career? It is also worthwhile to identify financial means, housing, coping mechanisms, socialization, and family and community support. Be familiar with the patient's current treatment such as day program, counseling, group therapy, rehabilitation program, medications, and psychiatric follow-up. Ask the patient if any of these interventions have helped.

Example:
Currently, how would you describe yourself?

I'm doing great. I've never been depressed since then, despite the fact that I stopped going to the group therapy. I just continued the pills my psychiatrist told me to take. I've also seen my counselor regularly and he has helped me cope.

That's good. Now that you're feeling great, how do you spend your day?

I usually go for walks, mostly one hour in the morning and thirty minutes in the afternoon. I take a nap in the afternoon. At night, I play bingo with my neighbors.

Suicidality or homicidality

In regular practice, we ask stable and asymptomatic patients only occasionally about having suicidal or homicidal thoughts. But in

33

this examination, asking the patient, even briefly, about self-destructive thoughts or recent violent tendencies may help demonstrate to the board examiner that you are thorough and careful.

Past Psychiatric History

The core components include: a) history of psychiatric illness, b) prior treatment, c) history of suicidality, homicidality and violence, d) alcohol and drug abuse or dependence and its treatment, e) sexual, physical, emotional and verbal abuse, and f) traumatic experience.

History of psychiatric illness

Determine prior psychiatric disorder, including symptoms that were undiagnosed or untreated. For a patient with a *simple* history, you just inquire about the prior episode as it happened. Ask about the psychiatric diagnosis or disorder, and if the patient cannot remember this, inquire about the predominant symptom. For patients with complicated history, i.e. those suffering from or having suffered from multiple diagnosis or disorders, you may inquire about all the disorders but you have to focus on the most disabling or predominant disorder, for instance, schizophrenia. Inquire about associated impairment in functioning and relational problems. In addition, ask about the precipitant of the illness such as loss of a job, divorce, or financial problems.

Example:
>   You mentioned a while ago that you've been depressed all your life. Tell me about that.

>   *I can't remember being happy when I was young. I felt different, out of place. I was not comfortable with friends. For every good event that happened, I just could not enjoy it. I felt I wanted to cry for no reason.*

34

Did you consult a mental health worker then?

I saw a psychiatrist. He was nice but I was not comfortable. So I decided to stop seeing him after the first session.

Did the doctor tell you what kind of illness you had?

He told me that I was depressed, that I had chemical imbalance.

Aside from feeling unhappy and wanting to cry, what other symptoms were you experiencing then?

I was so irritable. No one could mess with me. I easily snap. I could hardly sleep.

Prior treatment

Ask for any intervention undertaken to treat the illness. It is not uncommon to meet a patient with no prior treatment or hospitalization despite the presence of disabling symptoms. If no treatment was given, ask why. Has treatment been recommended by the physician or counsellor? If it was recommended, ask the reason for non-compliance.

A different strategy is required for patients with complicated histories – those with multiple diagnosis or symptoms, multiple hospitalizations or multiple medications. For a patient who has undergone multiple hospitalizations, ask first about the most recent hospitalization and its precipitant. If you still have time, inquire about the worst or longest hospitalization, or the hospitalization with the most impact on the patient. Regarding multiple trials of different medications, you may inquire about the names of all medications and discover the reason for changes in medications. Then focus on the most helpful ones. Response to and side effects from the drugs are noteworthy since you need to devise your treatment plan after the interview. Finally, ask about other types of intervention such as individual psychotherapy, group therapy, couples counselling, and rehabilitation.

Example:

When you were younger, what kind of help did you receive then?

I was then referred to a school counselor. I think I saw her once but that was it. When I was 21, my brother advised me to see a psychiatrist. I was then having a tough time after I lost my boyfriend in a car accident.

You mentioned seeing a psychiatrist, did he make any recommendation?

I was prescribed to take a "nerve pill." I hated pills so I didn't take it. After a few months, I felt better so the more I didn't have any reason to take it.

History of suicidality, homicidality, and violence

Any history of suicide or homicide ideation or behavior should be sought actively and its intensity, type, and circumstances determined. Given the time constraints of the examination, the question of dealing with multiple history of suicidal or homicidal behavior arises. Is it necessary to get a complete list of past ideation and attempts, and the circumstances behind them? While you need to be familiar particularly with types of suicidal and homicidal attempts, focus on the worst and most recent attempts and their trigger mechanisms.

Example:

Did you wish you were dead then?

Sort of. I thought then that nothing was going for me. I thought I was better off dead.

Did you attempt to hurt yourself then?

I tried to overdose on pills. I guess it wasn't enough. I slept the whole day. Nobody knew that I did it.

Were you hospitalized?

No. When I woke the next day I was still too tired to attend school. I just stayed in bed. I did not tell anyone that I did something to hurt myself.

Did you try to get help?

My friend advised me to see a psychiatrist. But as I told you, I didn't take the nerve pills.

Was that the first and last attempt to hurt yourself?

Yeah.

Alcohol and drug abuse or dependence and prior or current treatment

Establish the presence of alcohol and illicit drug problem. Know the amount, drug of choice, frequency of intake, duration, and associated withdrawal signs and symptoms. Obtain information about any impairment in personal, social, occupational, and marital functioning related to the excessive use. Determine the occurrence of legal problems and involvement in a variety of "addictive behavior" such as stealing and conning in order to sustain the habit. Ask about treatment such as AA, detoxification and rehabilitation programs.

Depending on factors of chronicity and amount of intake, the use of alcohol and illicit drugs results in psychological signs and symptoms. The need for accurate information on the possible abuse or dependence helps in the diagnosis and in treatment disposition. For instance, a patient with a long history of heavy alcohol drinking may experience severe depression requiring detoxification and sobriety for at least four weeks before an anti-depressant can be considered. A patient suffering from psychosis related to heavy use of cocaine may not necessarily require neuroleptic medications, although detoxification may be indicated.

As suggested by DSM IV, a four-week cut-off period should be used (American Psychiatric Association, 1994). Clarify whether the psychological signs and symptoms persist despite abstinence. Moreover, be aware that not all use of alcohol and drugs results in psychological problems, and infrequent and minimal use of alcohol or drugs makes it unlikely to be the culprit. By and large, the use is chronic and heavy when it gives rise to significant symptoms.

Do not hesitate to consider the possibility of a co-morbid disorder for someone with substance use who experiences psychological symptoms. A few clues exist for the presence of primary psychiatric disorder. If the psychiatric signs and symptom have preceded the use of alcohol or illicit drugs and if the psychiatric problem has persisted after a significant period of sobriety, it is likely that a primary psychiatric disorder exists (First et. al., 1995). Of course, a family history of mental illness may indicate the possibility of a primary psychiatric disorder.

Example:

>Some people who have been depressed for a while try to self-medicate or treat themselves by taking alcohol or street drugs. Have you ever done that?

>*In high school, I used to drink with my friends after class. But nothing recently. Alcohol makes me worse. It's not for me.*

>How about drugs?

I use hash once in a while.

Does it help you?

Sometimes I feel better.

How much do you use?

Perhaps, four joints a day.

How long have you been using it?

I've been using it since high school. But it has gotten worse lately.

Have you had any problem or been in trouble since you started using it?

No.

Have you used any other drug like cocaine or heroin?

No.

Sexual, physical, verbal, and emotional abuse; traumatic experience

Obtain information about experiences of abuse or trauma. Determine the type of abuse whether sexual, physical, or verbal/ emotional, the duration and frequency, the circumstances behind each episode, the perpetrator, and the associated emotional and functional impairment. Has there been any effort to seek help or tell anyone, including the authorities? How has the patient coped with the horrifying experience? Has anyone attempted to protect the patient? How does the family deal with the experience?

Prior episodes of abuse and trauma can predispose the individual to an emotional disorder. Borderline Personality Disorder (BPD), Acute Stress Disorder (ASD) and Posttraumatic Stress Disorder (PTSD) are known mental illnesses associated with past or recent abuse or trauma. Knowledge of prior abuse or trauma is thus helpful in the differential diagnosis. For instance, severe depression in the context of nightmares and prior abuse may indicate PTSD. On the other hand, mood instability and suicidal gestures associated with prior abuse point to the possibility of BPD.

Knowledge of prior abuse is also helpful in determining the appropriate treatment plan. Having a painful experience, such as sexual molestation, may make the individual a potential candidate for individual psychotherapy.

Example:

> Some people who have been depressed for a while were mistreated as children. Have you been mistreated physically by anyone?

> *My mom used to beat me in the head.*

> Tell me about that.

> *My mom was so controlling. If any of us wouldn't do what she wanted, she would lash out at us. Whenever she was mad, she would hit me in the head with a belt.*

> That's awful. How old were you when it all started?

> *I was so young then, perhaps four years old. She would hit me frequently for no reason, I think, almost every day. It only stopped when I was in grade twelve.*

> What made her stop?

My teacher in mathematics noticed the scars. I remember that we had a meeting with the principal. I don't know what exactly happened but I noticed that she changed since then.

Has anyone mistreated you in a sexual way?

My brother used to pinch me in my breast but nothing more than that.

TIPS

- **Focus on the core components in each section.**

- **Determine the predominant symptom that causes impairment and disability.**

- **Focus during interview on any information relevant to knowing the diagnosis, treatment recommendation, and on-going or chronic stressor.**

- **Prior psychiatric disorder should be determined, including symptoms that were undiagnosed or untreated.**

- **Determine patient's safety level.**

- **Consider the possibility of a co-morbid disorder in a patient suffering from substance abuse.**

- **Knowledge of prior abuse or trauma helps in the differential diagnosis and in determining the appropriate treatment plan.**

Obtain An Adequate History II

Past Medical History

The core components include a) prior or current medical, surgical, or neurological history, b) pregnancy, c) allergy, and d) medications.

Prior or current medical, surgical, or neurological history

In this section, you inquire about the presence of **common** medical or neurological problems that result in psychological problems. Ask about stroke, head trauma or injury, seizure disorder, CVA, thyroid disease, and so on. Stroke and thyroid disease are among the most common pathologies that result in referrals to psychiatry at the emergency room. A 70 year-old patient, for instance, was referred to me for treatment of acute depression. Apparently, the patient had been crying uncontrollably for 24 hours prior to ER evaluation. When I saw him, he presented with crying episodes and slurring of speech. I immediately recommended CT Scan of the Head that revealed an infarct. Another patient, a 56 year-old lady, came in with depression, psychomotor retardation and lack of energy. A laboratory screen showed a significantly high TSH level. She was immediately placed on thyroid medication and did very well after a few months. These cases show the need to consider the possibility of a medical condition as a cause of the psychological disturbance.

Example:

You mentioned that you don't have a lot of energy. Have you had any health problems that can explain it?

Three years ago, my family doctor diagnosed me with hypothyroidism. He put me on thyroxine. So far, my thyroid levels have been OK.

When was the last blood work done?

Two months ago and it was noted to be fine.

Any other illnesses such as head injury, epilepsy, heart, or liver problems that you may be suffering from?

No.

Aside from thyroxine, are there any other drugs you've been taking recently?

None.

Have you experienced any side effects from thyroxine?

No.

Note the presence of surgical procedures that the patient has previously undergone. Frequently, the surgical history sheds light on the psychiatric diagnosis and treatment disposition. For instance, a patient with prior thyroidectomy and currently presenting with depression and psychomotor retardation may actually be suffering from hypothyroidism requiring thyroid hormone replacement. Likewise, it is appropriate to explore the possibility of factitious disorder in a patient with multiple abdominal surgeries, especially if surgical indications are vague. Moreover, know the presence of physical illness that causes disability and functional impairment. These factors add more stress to the patient and family members and hence may require therapeutic intervention.

Pregnancy

In general, it is better to ask during the interview whether a female patient of childbearing age is pregnant. If you fail to ask about pregnancy status in the interview, recommend a pregnancy test during the presentation and discussion. Your treatment recommendation may be dependent upon the patient's pregnancy status. In your discussion, avoid recommending psychotropic medication for someone who is pregnant, especially in the first trimester. Mood stabilizers, for instance, have been known to cause a congenital anomaly such as spina bifida and Ebstein anomaly. There are instances wherein the use of medications may be warranted such as during severe psychosis or mania. Mention in your discussion that the risks and benefits of medication should be weighed and discussed with the patient. Appropriate alternative treatments to intake of medications, such as ECT, should be strongly considered.

Allergy

Inquiry about allergy may be necessary since a patient may have taken various kinds of medications in the past. It is possible that a few patients may have experienced allergic reaction. Knowledge of a reaction to psychotropic medications may guide you regarding which medication to suggest and which to avoid in the treatment plan.

I must emphasize that you should learn to differentiate an allergic reaction from drug side effects. Some patients acknowledge some reactions as allergy when they are in fact rare side effects of the drug such as acute dystonia and photosensitivity. In the discussion of your treatment plan, point out to the examiners that the patient needs education about the difference between a drug's side effects and allergic reactions.

Medications

Some drugs are infamous for contributing to emotional difficulties. Common examples include beta-blockers as a cause of depression and steroids as a cause of psychosis. Some drugs can worsen a patient's frustration, marital conflict, and emotional instability through their side effects. Patients who are taking cardiac medications, for example, should be evaluated for the presence of erectile dysfunction, which in turn can precipitate low self-esteem and poor relationships with their spouses.

Family History

Core components include: a) prior or current history of psychiatric illness, b) treatment, c) suicidality, homicidality, violence, and d) alcohol/drug abuse or dependence.

Prior or current history of psychiatric illness

The presence of psychiatric disorder in the family should be sought because knowledge of the patient's genetic predisposition can guide you with the diagnosis. Those patients who have been brought up by mentally ill parents or who have been raised with mentally ill siblings may have experienced severe stress and neglect in childhood, thus predisposing them to mental illness.

Example:

You mentioned a while ago that your mother used to hit you a lot as a child. Do you think that your mom might have suffered from an emotional problem?

She used to take "nerve pills." She was in and out of a psychiatric hospital but I don't know what she was suffering from. But I noticed then that she was so irritable. She'd shout at us or hit me with a belt for no reason. At night, she'd get agitated. Her demeanor would change in a strange way.

Did you notice her talking to herself then?

Occasionally.

Did she appear to be suspicious?

Very. She was suspicious of everything we did. She used to accuse me of anything.

Like what?

That I was sleeping with everyone in town including my father. At one time, she confronted me that I was the leader of a gang that was out to get her. It was crazy and very stressful.

Did she ever attempt to hurt herself?

I don't recall.

Besides hitting you with a belt, was there other violence at home?

Oh my. She had these spurts of aggression. That was when she would hit me bad on my head. One day I came from school and I saw her throwing things all over and banging the wall.

That must be scary.

It was terrible.

Anyone else in the family with mental illness?

My father used to drink a lot. I'm not sure if he was using drugs back then.

Do you think your father drank alcohol so heavily then?

He used to go home drunk. He would end up sleeping on the floor a lot of times. He couldn't work in the morning. His boss fired him eventually.

Treatment

The type of treatment received by the family member and the nature of response to it should guide you in your treatment recommendation. For example, if the mother of the patient has responded well to a particular type of medication, SSRI for example, it may be worthwhile to consider SSRI as the drug of choice for your depressed patient. On the other hand, if the patient's parents or siblings have a long history of non-response to a certain type of treatment, then such treatment should not be considered a priority.

Suicidality, homicidality, or violence; alcohol/drug abuse or dependence

Inquiry about suicidal/homicidal ideation or attempt and the use of alcohol and illicit drugs in the family can help tremendously in knowing any genetic predisposition to an illness. It may also reveal the type of stressor the patient has experienced. As you well know, a negative event, such as a family member committing suicide, or an alcoholic, abusive father physically assaulting a sibling is considered by many patients as traumatic experience. Such experience may lead to destructive attitudes and lifestyles. A patient exposed to violence as a child may consider assault and other forms of aggression as a way of dealing with the world. Through role modeling, actions such as suicide, violence, and aggression can be construed as a way to cope with frustrations and problems. Likewise, the use of alcohol may be viewed as a way of escaping from reality. Inquire as to how patients cope with present life challenges. Do they cope by such inappropriate means as aggression, passivity, and excessive use of alcohol/illicit drugs, or do they cope by more acceptable means such as counseling, conflict resolution, and learning problem-solving skills? Such knowledge can give you ideas about appropriate treatment recommendation such as individual psychotherapy and grief work.

Personal and Social History

The core components should include this mnemonic:

S	Schooling
E	Employment
R	Relationships
I	Interests
A	Abuse
L	Legal troubles

By the time you reach this stage, you have only a few minutes prior to the start of the formal MSE. Ideally, you need to get as much information as you can during the interview. In reality, you cannot obtain a great amount of information due to time constraints. Given this limitation, you cannot ask any questions without good justification. You must know clearly the reason why you are asking a certain question.

My suggestion is that you probe for any information that may be relevant 1) to clinch a diagnosis, 2) to better understand the interviewee's frame of mind, 3) to determine appropriate treatment recommendations, and 4) to identify on-going or chronic stressors. Based on the information you have gathered from prior sections, you now have a clue as to what areas may be important. For example, you need to explore the presence of abuse in a patient who appears to have some borderline features noted in the history. For someone having problems with memory, understanding, and communicating one's concerns, the history of school delay or special education may be considered. For patients with antisocial traits, as manifested by childhood behavioral problems and irresponsibility, it is worthwhile to ask about recent or past legal troubles.

Past experiences have shaped the minds of patients in certain ways. A person's worldview and character are considerably affected by trauma. For someone with a long history of mental illness, you may have to ask about the impact of the illness on relationships and employment. On the other hand, you may need to explore the impact of one's occupation on current mental illness. For patients with significant mental illness in the family, you need to know the impact of the parent's or sibling's illness on these patients' functioning while growing up.

Determine any ongoing relationship problems, marital conflict, sexual difficulties, and family or work-related violence that may have precipitated or maintained current or past emotional difficulties. Knowledge of psychosocial issues is crucial in making the appropriate treatment intervention.

Example:

> You told me before that your depression has affected your work. Tell me about that.

> *I just don't have any energy to work or do anything. I can't focus on what I do. As a result my performance has been sloppy. Occasionally, I had been absent. My boss has noticed the change in me. He suggested that I should get help.*

What kind of work you do?

I work as a secretary for the CEO of a company.

How long have you been working there?

Three years.

Before you worked for this company, did you attend any courses to prepare yourself for this type of job?

Yeah. I finished a two-year postgraduate course in Office Administration at a community college.

Mental Status Examination

Usually the board examiners will warn you when you have only five minutes left in the interview. Once you hear this warning, start your examination of the mental status. Dr. David Robinson, in his new book Mnemonics and More for Psychiatry, provides a simplified way of remembering the vital components of MSE: **ABC STAMP LICKER**

> **A**PPEARANCE
> **B**EHAVIOR
> **C**OOPERATION
>
> **S**PEECH
> **T**HOUGHT
> **A**FFECT
> **M**OOD
> **P**ERCEPTION
>
> **L**EVEL OF CONSCIOUSNESS

INSIGHT AND JUDGMENT
COGNITIVE FUNCTIONING AND
SENSORIUM
KNOWLEDGE BASE
ENDINGS
RELIABILITY

Significant MSE findings can be known during the interview and prior to the "actual" mental status examination. In clinical practice, once enough information about the MSE is obtained, a formal MSE is usually cut short partly due to time constraints. However, in this examination, you still need to do the formal MSE to show your thoroughness to the board examiner. Know additional information necessary to make a suitable differential diagnosis.

Some of the findings here are diagnostic of a particular mental illness and hence are decisive in the differential diagnosis. A patient who appears disheveled, with slow movement, impaired posture, and poor grooming may have a psychotic, cognitive or mood disorder. A seductive patient wearing sunglasses inside the interview room and exhibiting an exaggerated manner of speech may possess histrionic traits. A borderline trait may apply to someone with multiple, superficial scars on the forearm, with a tattoo on the right leg and a ring dangling from the nose. Likewise, a patient who demonstrates rapid and loud speech associated with irritability may suffer from mania. Finally, a person with looseness of association along with flat affect may have a psychotic disorder.

The extent of your MSE is tailored to your findings in the initial part of the interview. If the patient complains of paranoia, it is worthwhile to probe in detail for the presence of bizarre delusions and auditory/ visual hallucinations. For patients with complaints of memory lapses, a test for abstract reasoning, immediate and recent memory, executive functioning, aphasia, apraxia and agnosia should be part of the detailed examination. If time is tight, focus on the presenting problem and get the necessary detail. If enough time is available, you may proceed to address additional MSE issues such as the presence of intrusive thoughts, compulsive behavior, and hypothetical testing for judgment.

Example:

> Let me shift gears now and I'll formally test your memory and how you think. In this section, I am going to ask you routine questions we usually ask patients. Ok?

> *Ok.*

> Tell me the date today?

> *June 15.*

> What's the day of the week?

> *Friday.*

BUDGET YOUR TIME

Budgeting your time appropriately is a core component of this interview. Spending too much time in one section, such as HPI, medical history, or personal and social history may detract from establishing the right diagnosis and from understanding the real concerns and problems of the patient. As opposed to the suggestions of most review courses that divide the thirty-minute period into several parts to deal with each section (such as eight minutes for HPI, five minutes for PPH, etc.), I suggest that you divide your interview into three parts only. The first fifteen minutes are devoted to introduction, HPI, and PPH. The next ten minutes focus on PMH, FH, and PSH. And the last five minutes deal with the formal MSE.

As I have noted earlier, this strategy reduces frequent glances at your watch and significantly improves eye contact with the patient. There are some advantages of frequent eye contact. Such contact conveys to the patient that you are listening to what he or she has to say. It shows the examiner that you are more concerned with the person rather than simply obtaining information. Furthermore, it also improves and maintains rapport and alliance because of the feeling of importance and the attention it gives to the patient. On the other hand, frequent glances at your watch create disadvantages, including more distraction, less rapport, and more preoccupation with time than with the person.

In budgeting your time, it is also important to use wisely the full thirty-minute period. Occasionally, a few candidates terminate the interview prematurely, such as at 15 or 20 minutes, then stating that he or she has no more questions to ask. Such untimely conclusion can be caused by extreme anxiety or perhaps arrogance. This unfortunate approach, regardless of the cause, invites failure.

BEGIN THE MENTAL STATUS EXAMINATION PRIOR TO FORMAL MSE

Although I designate the last five minutes for MSE, in reality the MSE starts from the very beginning – from the introduction with your first handshake, during HPI, PMH, FH, and PSH and down to the last five minutes of the interview. A lot of the MSE findings are given "for free" during the interview (Morrison and Munoz, 1996). Any abnormalities in the patient's appearance, behavior, cooperation, speech, affect, thought form, level of consciousness, insight and judgment, and knowledge base can be known prior to the last five minutes or the MSE part of the interview. Your mind must remain active in making observations. If possible, you can do some of the MSE while the patient is still in the waiting room. This strategy allows you to optimize the use of your time.

During the introduction and history-taking phase prior to actual MSE, meticulously observe the patient for any remarkable findings. Body piercing, tattoos, and colorful and unusual hairstyles may indicate certain personality traits. While disheveled appearance, blunted affect, disorganized behavior, or catatonia may indicate a primary psychotic disorder, psychomotor retardation may indicate clinical depression. Even the first handshake is helpful in determining the ongoing clinical problem. Sweaty and cold palms may indicate the presence of an anxiety disorder.

During the interview, speech and memory problems may be determined. A slow, monotonous speech pattern may indicate depression while a disorganized speech pattern may point to a primary psychotic disorder. Memory can be indirectly assessed by listening intently to the patient's recollection of personal issues, concerns, medications, and history of emotional problems.

TIPS

- **Determine the presence of common medical or neurological problems that result in psychological problems.**

- **The surgical history sheds light on the psychiatric diagnosis and treatment disposition.**

- **Patient's genetic predisposition can guide you with the diagnosis.**

- **Knowledge of psychosocial issues is helpful in identifying the appropriate treatment plan.**

- **You need to do the formal MSE to show your thoroughness to the board examiner.**

- **Budget your time appropriately without compromising frequent eye contact.**

- **Begin the mental status examination at the start of the interview.**

CHAPTER *5*

History-Taking Techniques

LEARN TO REDIRECT THOSE ASTRAY

Some patients have a tendency to talk too much about their concerns and problems frequently without being asked. Some talk extensively in response to a particular question and at times jump from one topic to another with ease, as your precious thirty minutes slip away. This situation is common and has to be dealt with appropriately if you desire to obtain enough information to make a diagnosis and get an adequate history. There are several techniques that I find useful.

Interrupt the flow

When the patient starts to ramble, depleting your precious time, you need to interrupt in a polite and acceptable way. Do not stop the interviewee by raising a red flag or by simply saying "stop" in a loud voice. Be gentle and considerate. There are a few ways of interrupting the patient genially.

A. Acknowledge the importance of the topic or concern. Tell the patient that the topic raised is very important and that you may return to this topic if time permits. Then refer the patient back to the previous topic or start a new topic.

Example:

As a child, my classmates used to pick on me. They called me "fatso, slow, teacher's pet" and other humiliating names. I used to keep the pain inside because each time I told my teacher, he just ignored me. (Patient has been talking more than 7 minutes in the PSH alone.)

It really sounds very important to talk about that. Let's talk about this later if we have more time. A while ago, we were talking about your depressed mom. Tell me more about that.

B. Recognize the patient's emotion and then empathize. You may recognize the patient's feelings at that time and use empathic statements or a pause if necessary. Then refer the patient back to the previous topic or start a new topic.

Example:

Can you imagine? They accused me of stealing when I didn't do anything! I'm gonna get back at them. I'm gonna sue them if they continue to harass me. I'm tired of this. Patient cried. (Patient has been talking freely for more than five minutes.)

Pause . . .(for a few seconds) . . .You sound very angry and upset. We were talking about your girlfriend a while ago. Why don't we talk about your relationship with your girlfriend prior to this legal trouble?

C. Direct the patient's attention to your interest and state that there's a lack of time. Tell the patient that you are interested in the current topic but add that time is running out. Refer the patient back to the previous topic or start a new topic.

Example:

I love basketball. I saw the Spurs against Lakers last night and it was great. You see the styles of Shaq and Kobe? Man, I tell you. You better watch it. Since I was small, I've been so involved with it. I watch TV all night, nonstop. (Patient has been talking about basketball for several minutes when asked about his hobbies.)

That sounds interesting! Unfortunately, time is running out. Tell me about your profession.

Return smoothly to the prior topic or start a new topic.

After you have successfully interrupted the patient's flow, then you obtain the necessary information needed to clinch the diagnosis, to determine a life pattern, and to get an adequate history. In summary, there are two ways of doing this. You may return smoothly to the prior topic. Do this if you have not obtained adequate information about that topic. You may start a new topic. At some point you do this because you still need to get more information about other sections of the history, and you feel you need more details about the person's illness and concerns. If a rambling patient uses up your precious time, you have to act and then make use of the remaining time.

ESTABLISH RELATIONSHIP BETWEEN EVENTS

This part of the interview refers to a detailed exploration of possible causes and consequences, of possible indirect and direct links between events. Ask patients about the predominant symptom, associated signs and symptoms, and the precipitant and consequences of the illness. If, for example, the patient complains of depression, ask about the presence of stressors that precipitated it. Inquire also about any emotional and physical problems that can be linked to the symptoms. Moreover, find out about the consequences of the illness to the person's interpersonal, personal, and occupational functioning. In establishing a relationship between events, you may use such phrases as: *as a result of . . . , due to . . . , because of . . . , what was going on in your life at that time . . .* , among others.

Example:

I have been very depressed. Every morning when I wake up, I feel something strange inside; it's kind of a queer feeling. I don't know how to explain it.

What was going on in your life at that time?

Two months before the depression started, I caught my husband in bed with another woman. She was our neighbor. I didn't know that he was doing this to me.

You must have been shocked about what you saw.

Yeah. I was very upset.

As a result of the depression, what has happened to your functioning?

I couldn't do anything. I just didn't want to get up from bed. I felt drained and very weak.

ALLOW PATIENT TO TALK

In the interview we usually allow the patient to talk "freely" during the first few minutes. This "free talk" phase allows the individual to talk spontaneously about preoccupations and concerns. There are good reasons for using free talk. First, you get a "bird's eye view" of the patient's concerns and emotional status. Through free talk, patients are allowed to talk about what is important to them such as a job loss that has resulted in emotional difficulties, or vice versa. In this way, you can assess the patient early for any obvious pathology such as paranoia, pressured speech, formal thought disorder and the like. Secondly, "free talk" is potentially an icebreaker. It builds an alliance with the patient by giving the person a feeling of importance through an unrestricted expression of one's problems, concerns, and emotion. Thirdly, as Drs. Morrison and Munoz pointed out, free speech may help the patient "to relax and to confide in you."

Free talk can be facilitated by the use of open-ended questions. In clinical practice, we tend to use open-ended questions liberally because we have sufficient time to explore a patient's concerns. You can devote longer period or extra sessions to do a comprehensive patient's evaluation. But in the psychiatry oral exam you are limited to a thirty-minute period and do not have the luxury to use open-ended questions frequently. However, you can still use them if necessary. Certainly you can use open-ended questions in any part of the interview when you want to know some details about areas such as abuse and relationships.

Some review courses or supervisors have suggested limiting the use of open-ended questions to the free talk phase because of inadequate time. I disagree with this suggestion since the overuse of close-ended questions will make you appear boring and seemingly interested only with the DSM IV criteria.

Some phrases that facilitate free talk: tell me about. . . , what. . . , how. . . , among others.

Example:
What brought you to treatment?

I don't know. I just felt drained. I don't have any interest to do anything. I used to love going to the mall and working in my garden. But now I don't have any of that. I prefer to stay in the corner of my room and not go anywhere. I hate to talk to people. I do not want to answer phone calls. It all started when I saw my husband with another woman.

Tell me about that.

It happened two months ago. I caught him in bed with another woman. She was our neighbor and a good friend. Now I know why she visited us very often.

Another way of facilitating free talk is through active listening. Listening in a manner that shows your interest in the patient's concerns and issues is a useful skill to develop. Frequent eye contact and remarks acknowledging the person's predicament such as *I see, it's too bad,* and *I know* are constructive ways of encouraging the patient to talk. Facilitate the patient's story and description of mental anguish through proper gestures such as head nodding. Brief comments such as *oh my, yeah,* and *uh oh* encourage the patient to communicate highly charged emotions. The patient is likely to appreciate your gesture, and the process may strengthen the rapport initially established in the first few minutes of the interview.

DEAL EFFECTIVELY WITH DIFFICULT PATIENTS

The psychiatry oral exam is stressful enough. Having a difficult patient adds more to the challenge. One typical problem concerns the individual, who after staying quietly in the interview room for only five to ten minutes, suddenly leaves the room without any warning. The examinee is left in the room and feels anxious about what is going to happen next. Meanwhile, the board examiners are waiting for the exam candidate to present the case in a professional manner. This dilemma actually happened to two of my colleagues. And it could happen to you.

My two colleagues dealt with this ordeal through a detailed observation of the patient. Since they did not have any history to present, due to the patient's inability and unwillingness to respond to the questions, they relied heavily on the MSE. They discussed in a logical manner: a) appearance e.g. disheveled, malodorous, b) behavior e.g. agitation, distress, c) cooperation d) abnormal movements such as pill-rolling tremors, akinesia, akathisia, e) speech e.g. mute, impoverished, f) possible thought content such as paranoia or thought form disorder, g.) affect e.g. flat, constricted, inappropriate, h) possible mood e.g. irritable, i) perception e.g. response to internal stimuli, j) level of consciousness such as alert, drowsy, k) insight and judgment and other aspects of mental status examination. In their presentations, they discussed a detailed MSE and the possible differential diagnosis based on the significant findings. Both of them passed the examination in one sitting.

A second type of problem concerns the typical mute or seemingly uncooperative patient who refuses to respond to all your questions, while intending to stay in the patient room during the full length of the interview. My supervisors and Dr. Shea, the author of Psychiatric Interviewing: The Art of Understanding, have suggested the strategy of asking open-ended questions repeatedly until the patient starts to talk. You may use frequently *how* and *what* questions such as *how do you feel about being here? what's bothering you at this time? what brought you to treatment?* Let the patient *describe* and *tell* one's experience or concerns. For example: *tell me about your problems* or *describe to me how you spend your day.* Other supervisors have advised me to identify something unique or striking about the unresponsive patient and try to elicit a response. For example: *Your eyeglasses seem to fit you well. Where did you buy them?* Or: *You look upset today. What is going on in your life right now?*

In a review course, one mentor advised to ask for the patient's "best time of his or her life" in the hope that the patient would respond.

A third category of difficult patient involves the individual who demonstrates pressured speech associated with other manic symptoms. For this type of patient, close-ended questions are more appropriate, after a few minutes of initial "free talk"(Morrison, 1995). Once a question is answered, ask the next close-ended question. Try not to allow the patient to change the topic without your prompting.

GIVE EMPATHIC STATEMENTS OR GESTURES GENEROUSLY

In dealing with patients in clinical practice or with people in other contexts, constantly learn the art of showing empathy, especially through the use of empathic statements. Important to empathy is the ability to recognize the patient's feelings or emotional difficulties and to convey your awareness of them effectively to the patient. Some helpful empathic statements include: *you sound very upset. . ., that must have been difficult for you. . . ,*and *that's terrible.*

Example:

> *My mom left us when we were small. She left with another man. My dad ended up drinking a lot every day. When he got home, he'd yell at us, and would call me names. I was left taking care of my sisters and a brother . . .*(crying) *. . . Nobody bothered to help.*

You sound very upset that nobody seemed to care.

You can show empathy by recognizing the situation of the patient and then by letting the patient know that you recognize it.

Example:

> *I was only 15 then and yet I had a lot of responsibilities. I had to make sure that my younger brother and sisters go to school. I had to work at McDonald's to make sure that there was food on the table. Meanwhile, my dad just continued to be drunk.*

It was a difficult moment for you.

A powerful way of conveying your empathy is through the use of pauses. This gesture, if used properly, may encourage the patient to open up and talk about the emotional difficulty and its circumstances.

Example:

> *One night while everyone was asleep, my dad came home drunk. He went to his room and asked for coffee. After I gave him the coffee, he held my hand so tight that I couldn't move. He pushed me down to his bed* . . .(crying) . . . *then* . . . (crying). .

Pause before answering or asking a question.

Offering a tissue during a tense and tearful episode is an empathic gesture highly recommended by a lot of clinical supervisors and mock reviewers.

USE CLOSE-ENDED QUESTIONS APPROPRIATELY

Knowing when to use close-ended questions is just as important as knowing when to use open-ended ones. There are clinical situations that warrant the use of this type of questioning. Patients who show rapid speech patterns and who switch easily from one topic to another need the structure and limitation of a close-ended inquiry. For patients who respond spontaneously and provide details with ease, close-ended questions may help you get information needed for prognostication and diagnostic purposes. Given time constraints, asking a close-ended question can help you focus on details necessary to build a strong differential diagnosis.

Close-ended questions also help in getting more details from the interviewee about sensitive areas such as abuse and self-destructive behavior.

Example:

You mentioned that your father pushed you onto the bed one night. What happened next?

... (Patient could not respond. She was sobbing.)...

Did he touch you on your private parts?

... (Patient remained quiet but she nodded her head and she continued to sob)...

It was certainly a difficult time for you ... (Pause)... Did he rape you?

(Patient sobbed ... after a few minutes, she calmed down and answered.) *Yes.*

As in the example above, any areas in one's life that cannot be expressed openly, because of guilt, fear, shame, and a state of denial, can be elicited effectively through using a close-ended question.

Close-ended questions are also helpful during the mental state examination and cognitive assessment (Morrison, 1995). Cognitive tests, such as tests for memory and orientation, require definite and short answers. Some of the sections in the MSE, such as the presence of suicidal or homicidal thoughts, obsession or compulsions, can be answered appropriately by yes or no.

MAINTAIN INTERVIEW IN A CONVERSATIONAL FORMAT

In any type of interview, you try to avoid appearing stiff and boring and asking mostly close-ended questions during your interview may contribute to monotony. Although close-ended questions can be very helpful, as shown above, overusing them docs not work in your favor. Many supervisors and review courses recommend their use after the "free talk" phase. This technique may be appropriate for someone who is overly talkative or who elaborates on a topic without much prompting. However, not all patients are like this. Some of them give only one-word answers and these answers, such as "I don't know" or "maybe," are not necessarily what you want.

I would suggest that you maintain your interview in a more "conversational" manner so that you strike a balance between "being interesting" and "being interested" in what the patient has to say. Doing your interview in a conversational format means simply switching from open-ended to close-ended questions and vice versa during the whole interview. Do not limit your open-ended questions to the free talk phase and do not relegate the use of close-ended questions to the period after the HPI. How often do you have to switch? It depends upon the patient, the topic, and the time available. If time is a problem, try not to over utilize open-ended questions so that you can cover other important sections in the history.

The conversational format may be applicable to patients who are not very spontaneous and who prefer not to elaborate on certain topics.

Example: (Family History)
>You mentioned your parents a while ago. Are there any emotional problems in your family?

>*My sister told me that my mom was taking pills for her "nerves."*

Tell me about that.

I guess she was depressed.

How do you mean?

Well, I remember that she used to cry a lot for no reason. She would just lie down on the sofa, not doing anything the whole day. She would not eat and could not sleep at night.

I see. Did she ever attempt to hurt herself then?

No.

The conversational format may also be very helpful in pursuing very sensitive topics such as suicidal or homicidal behavior, and abuse.

Example: (Past Psychiatric History)
Some people who suffer from depression have thought about hurting themselves or have tried to do so. Have you ever attempted to hurt yourself?

Yeah.

Tell me about that.

I cut my wrist two years ago.

What was happening in your life then that made you do it?

My boyfriend and I broke up. He was the only person who seemed to understand me. But I learned that he was fooling around.

It was a difficult time for you. After you cut your wrist, were you hospitalized then?

They let me go. They thought I wasn't that bad.

USE TRANSITIONS WELL

If you listen carefully to a casual conversation in a group or between two friends, you will easily notice a smooth, effortless flow from one topic to another. Laughter, whispers, tears, or giggling mix with language, but in general most conversations flow gracefully. If you look deeper, you realize that they do not happen by chance. Most conversations follow certain powerful rules of communication that are not fully given to consciousness.

Most of these interesting communication patterns use "gates" or transitions. Gates or transitions are used to shift from area to another. For our purpose, these gates refer to switching from one section of the history to the next. Effective psychiatric interviews, like interesting conversation, follow the same rules of communication. Dr. Shea (1999), the author of Psychiatric Interviewing: The Art of Understanding, states that some of these transitions or "gates," when used properly during the interview, can promote a productive exchange. One clinical supervisor in residency gave me a piece of advice about interviewing. He said, "You know that an interview is effective if the patient does not feel being interviewed." The effective use of transitions can make your interview appear conversational.

Although Dr. Shea outlines numerous types of gates, I would like to emphasize the use of four types that will help make your interview during examination or in clinical practice more effective. The natural gate is described by Dr. Shea as a graceful flow of an interview from one area of interest to another, usually initiated by the interviewer.

Example:
   You said that your neighbor is out to get you?

Oh yeah. He's been spying on me since I moved here. Yesterday, he placed a tiny TV monitor on the walls so he could easily watch me. I feel trapped. It's scary knowing that my phone is bugged.

Some people who feel that neighbors are out to get them also suffer from unusual experiences such as voices saying bad things about them. Have you heard voices, and when you turn your head around there's no one there?

Sometimes.

In this example, the interviewer moved from delusion to hallucination, a closely related topic, through the use of the statement *some people who feel that neighbors are out to get them.* As you can see, the transition is smoothly done.

The referred gate is a smooth transition in which a new area of interest is introduced by referring to a previous topic mentioned in the interview (Shea, 1999).

Example:

> *My childhood was tough. I never felt love. Food was not enough for eight children. My father was never around because he worked overseas.*

A while ago you mentioned your mother. Tell me about any emotional problem that she may be suffering from.

My mom took nerve pills and was hospitalized a few times.

The interviewer attempted to move smoothly from personal and social history (*person's childhood and how tough it was*) to family history (*inquiry about family's emotional problem*) by using a previous topic (*mother*) mentioned earlier in the interview.

The implied gate is referred to by Dr. Shea (1999) as a graceful transition introduced by the interviewer who leaves one area of interest by "discussing about a closely associated topic that seems to follow from the conversation."

Example:

So you've been depressed?

I don't know why I've been feeling like this. There's no reason for me to be depressed. I have everything I need. I have a loving family, nice job, and luxury cars. I'm respected in the community where I live. And yet here I am. I don't see myself as having any worth.

Do you feel as though life is not worth living anymore?

At times, there's this thing inside me that tells me I'm no good, that I'm better off dead.

Have you heard voices that are not there?

In this example, the clinician took the opportunity to ask about the presence of auditory hallucination after the patient verbalized the statement *there's this thing inside me that tells me I'm no good* which could imply that something else is going on.

And lastly, the introduced gate refers to the interviewer's way of notifying the interviewee that there will be a change of topic.

Example:

I think I know a fair bit about you. Let me now ask you about your family. Is there any mental illness in the family?

My aunt was hospitalized at a mental hospital when I was ten years old.

The clinician, in this example, clearly stated his intention to move to another area of the patient's life before asking questions.

SUCCESSFUL USE OF ORGANIZING TOOLS

An effective psychiatric interview requires memory aids and structure to help you focus on the necessary information to be obtained in each section or for each DSM IV criterion. Several organizing tools such as an outline, checklist, and mnemonics or other memory aids can be utilized to help create a coherent interview.

Establishing an outline representing the major sections of the psychiatric history may simplify the interview process. As articulated by several texts and authors, you may organize your questions based on the following sections:

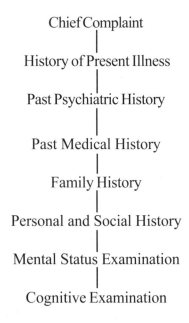

Chief Complaint

History of Present Illness

Past Psychiatric History

Past Medical History

Family History

Personal and Social History

Mental Status Examination

Cognitive Examination

It may prove beneficial to follow this format during the interview. The importance of focusing on one section until enough information is obtained, before moving to the next section, cannot be overemphasized.

Moreover, a checklist containing the important components of each section can be noteworthy and can help tremendously in organizing your interview. A checklist, such as the one found in the appendix, is not meant to be memorized but should serve as a guide.

In terms of mnemonics and memory aids, there are several existing mnemonics such as SIG E CAPS for major depressive disorder, and SERIAL for personal and social history that you can easily use. Dr. Robinson's new book Mnemonics and More for Psychiatry provides you with numerous helpful mnemonics such as ABC STAMP LICKER for MSE. However, you may need to devise your own mnemonic or memory aid since no single one fits every psychiatrist, given the variation in study techniques and long-term learning habits.

TACTFULLY TERMINATE THE INTERVIEW

Terminating the interview should be done in style, leaving an imprint of an impressive exit to both the examiners and the patient. Once the examiners signal stop, you should smoothly stop the interview. Like making an impressive entry in the introduction phase, there are ways of making a dynamic exit.

Thank the patient again for participation. A simple gesture like this shows considerable respect for the patient. Remember that the patient has made a sacrifice by allowing himself or herself to be subjected to repetitive questioning and to an unavoidable revisit of one's painful past. Although the patient receives a payment for the appearance, the amount given is minimal. In my opinion, some patients participate in testing the psychiatrists for non-monetary reasons such as the obligation to help.

You also consider shaking the hand of the patient and giving a genuine smile during the process. Show your gratitude. By hand gesture, lead the patient to the door without rushing. Throughout this phase, continue to be graceful. Do not forget that the alliance should be maintained even after the interview.

TIPS

- **Learn to deal with disorganized patients.**

- **Facilitate free talk by the use of open-ended questions.**

- **Deal effectively with difficult patients.**

- **Show empathy through appropriate gestures and statements.**

- **Some clinical situations warrant the use of close-ended questions.**

- **Maintain interview in a conversational format, that is, switching from open-ended to close-ended questions and vice versa during the whole length of the interview.**

- **Use transitions well to facilitate the smooth flow from one topic to the next.**

- **Use organizing tools such as an outline, mnemonic, checklist and other memory aids to help you focus on the necessary information.**

- **Terminate the interview in a respectful way.**

- **Show your concern and interest through active listening.**

PART II

ORGANIZE YOUR PRESENTATION

In your presentation as in your interview, think about the end or goal in mind. The goal is to present the case in an organized fashion, to establish the diagnosis in a logical manner, to offer a reasonable treatment plan and to give a more accurate prognosis. Provide details and relevant materials, including pertinent positives and negatives, which support your diagnosis, treatment plan and prognosis. You edit information in this section. Only essential information should be discussed in the appropriate sections and the unnecessary data should be discarded. A choice of useful strategies, such as effective use of chronology statements and templates, is discussed in the next chapters.

CHAPTER **6**

Three Approaches For A Better Presentation

Several techniques are useful in tackling the presentation part of the oral examination. These techniques help keep a smooth flow of ideas, show sequence in time, and help the listener follow your thoughts easily. Use these three techniques: 1) chronology statements, 2) transitional words and phrases, and 3) pronouncements.

CHRONOLOGY STATEMENTS

The oral presentation requires a chronological description of events in order to create a smooth flow from one area of interest to another. Chronology statements refer to the use of words or groups of words to indicate a time period in your presentation of the patient's history. These statements present facts and tell the story in sequence, leading you from one moment in time to the next. Examples include: *the patient was apparently well until about two weeks ago when; the symptoms persisted until about five days ago when; three months prior to consultation; about a week before the hospitalization.* These chronology statements highlight any

77

significant changes in the course of treatment, changes in the patient's clinical status such as worsening or improvement of the symptoms, and the reason for the changes such as a new stressor or receipt of treatment. Such a statement is also able to establish the occurrence of any stressors relevant to the change in status.

Example:

Inpatient:

The patient was apparently well until about four weeks ago when she began to feel depressed. She reported that she gradually became irritable over even the most trivial things. She said that she could easily snap at her children, especially during the busy morning prior to going to school. She also noticed that she could hardly focus on her usual morning chores. The symptoms persisted until about fourteen days ago when the patient began to experience thoughts that she never entertained before. She stated that she felt so empty that she preferred to die rather than to live. She thought that her neighbors were actually watching her moves in the bathroom. She could hardly sleep at night and her appetite got so bad that she lost a lot of weight. A day prior to hospitalization, the patient heard the voice of her deceased husband, telling her to join him in heaven. Her relatives saw her talking to herself. Hence, her relatives brought her to the hospital.

In this example, the chronology statement *the patient was apparently well until four weeks ago* has established the transition from the normal state to the start of the patient's depression. Likewise, the next chronology statements show the gradual change in clinical status eventually resulting in hospitalization.

Outpatient:

The patient was apparently his usual self until about three weeks prior to consultation when he discovered that his wife was having an affair with his best friend. He caught them in the mall holding hands and acting very romantic. He felt so bad but he decided not to confront her in order to avoid embarrassment. When she got home past midnight, he asked her to explain what he saw. To his surprise, she told him that she wanted out of the relationship. She revealed that she was having an affair for seven years with his best friend. The patient felt betrayed and upset. He could not eat that night. The next day, he lost his appetite and could not focus on his work. The patient still could not believe what happened, until about a week ago when she finally packed her bags, secured her cash, then left without a word. He felt lost and depressed. He did not know what to do. He could not go to work since he was shaking terribly. For no apparent reason, he just preferred to stay in bed the whole day. He felt as if he wanted to cry all the time. Two days prior to consultation, his neighbors got very concerned when he was seen disheveled and not going to work. His neighbors intervened and advised him to go to the nearest mental health clinic in the area. He then sought the help of the psychiatrist in the area who put him on SSRIs after evaluation.

The chronology statements *three weeks prior to consultation, the next day, a week ago, two days prior to consultation* have shown the successive change of events from the patient's usual emotional status to the occurrence of the stressor – his wife having an affair resulting eventually in her departure – and the unfortunate deterioration of his functioning.

TRANSITIONAL WORDS AND PHRASES

In their book Writing Clearly, Janet Lane and Ellen Lange explain the effective use of transitional words and phrases in articulating ideas. Transitional words and phrases refer to the use of words or groups of words that facilitate a smooth flow from one idea to the next. Transitions, such as *moreover, furthermore, additionally,* announce additional information. Transitions may show a sequence in time, for example: *consequently, subsequently, eventually, afterward;* they indicate a result or consequence of an event, for example: *as a result, as a consequence, accordingly;* they announce an example such as *for example, for instance among others;* and they reveal a contrast such as *however, in contrast, instead.* Transitions provide coherent links between ideas and establish time relationships (Lane and Lange, 1999).

When used effectively during presentation, transitions create a smooth flow from one idea, topic, or section of the history to the next. Just as in written literature, transitions in presentation provide additional information, may show sequence in time, give an example, and so on.

Example 1:

> *The patient reported that she had been experiencing panic attacks when she drove her car to work. She described each episode as a terrible feeling lasting for about ten minutes, with associated choking sensation, dizziness, palpitations, and trembling. Moreover, she stated that she developed extreme fear of being in a crowd of people. She related the difficulty of falling in line to pay for her groceries. Subsequently, she began to notice that the panic attacks had occurred at work frequently. She feared meeting her colleagues. She thought that if she ever developed the panic attacks, she would be humiliated in front of them. As a result of the above problems, she developed severe distress along with an inability to function well as a secretary, since the job entailed meeting new faces daily. Eventually, her colleagues began to notice a change in her behavior. Her job performance became dismal. After advice from her boss, she then developed the courage to see a psychiatrist for further evaluation and treatment.*

Example 2:

> *The patient was apparently doing well until about three months ago when his live-in girlfriend left him for another man. He said that their relationship turned sour gradually as she would make excuses to be away one or two weeks at a time. He began to be suspicious and questioned her whereabouts. She eventually packed up her bags and left, leaving a note seeking end of their ten-year relationship. As a result of her leaving, the patient became angry and despondent. Since she left, he could hardly focus on his job. He became erratic to the consternation of his co-workers. At night, he could hardly sleep. About two months ago, he was encouraged to seek professional help by trusted friends. He saw his family doctor who put him on an antidepressant. He was also referred to a psychologist for counseling who advised him to take a few days off from work. A few weeks later, his mood became better. He felt less irritable and less depressed. Moreover, he was able to sleep and focus well. His energy level slowly increased. Subsequently, he returned to work without any untoward incidents.*

In the examples above, the use of transitional words and phrases and chronology make a difference in keeping a smooth flow, showing a clear direction, and making the history easier to understand. Without these techniques, confusion easily ensues.

PRONOUNCEMENTS

Pronouncements refer to the clear announcement of a shift from one area of the history to another. This technique involves the use of words or phrases to introduce a new topic. Statements such as *in terms of, regarding, with regard to,* and *with respect to* are good examples.

Example 1:

The patient is a 40 y/o male who was referred for treatment by his psychologist due to worsening depression.

In terms of history of present illness, *the patient was apparently doing well until about three months ago when his live-in girlfriend left him for another man. He said that their relationship turned sour gradually as she would make excuses to be away one week or two weeks at a time. He began to be suspicious and questioned her whereabouts. She eventually packed up her bags and left, leaving a note seeking divorce. As a result of her leaving, the patient became angry and despondent. Since she left, he could hardly focus on his job. He became erratic to the consternation of his co-workers. At night he could hardly sleep. About two months ago, he was encouraged to seek professional help by trusted friends. He saw his family doctor who put him on an antidepressant. He was also referred to a psychologist for counseling who advised him to take off a few days from work. A few weeks later, his mood became better. He felt less irritable and less depressed. Moreover, he was able to sleep and focus well. His energy level slowly increased. Subsequently, he returned to work without any untoward incidents.*

Regarding past psychiatric history, *the patient denied having any significant emotional problems or treatment prior to this episode. He never had any period in his life where he thought of hurting himself or others. He said that he always had good coping skills with good support systems. He further denied use of any mood-altering substances such as alcohol or drugs.*

With respect to past medical history, *he told me that he had a cholecystectomy while in college but he had been*

82

healthy ever since. He denied prior history of head trauma or injury, seizure disorder, thyroid disease, and so on.

You can use the same technique during your whole presentation for identifying data, case formulation, differential diagnosis, and prognosis. This pronouncement technique helps delineate one topic from another and creates a smooth link between two sections in the history. Finally, it serves as a warning that a transition is about to occur.

TIPS

- **Chronological description of events is required to create a smooth flow from one area of interest to the next.**

- **Chronology statement should highlight any significant changes in the course of treatment and clinical status.**

- **Transitional words or phrases have a significant role in organizing your presentation.**

- **Transitions in presentation can perform various functions such as add information, show sequence in time, and give an example.**

- **Pronouncements help delineate one topic from another and warn that a transition is about to occur.**

- **You can combine transitions, pronouncement, and chronology statements to keep a smooth flow and to show a clear direction.**

CHAPTER 7

Effective Use Of Templates And Other Organizing Tools

Templates are organizing tools that you can use to structure your presentation. A template is a rack on which to hang data, a skeleton where muscles of information can be arranged. Construct templates that contain the core components of each section you wish to obtain during the interview. Keep in mind that the templates should fit your unique interview style and strategies and that they are not necessarily designed to be memorized.

History of Present Illness

Patients With Clear-Cut History:

Sample template:

Mr./Mrs./Ms._____ is a ___year old male/female who was apparently well until about _____ago (duration) when he/she started to experience_____(symptom). Such_____(symptom) was precipitated by_____(stress – give details). _____(duration) PTA, patient developed the following associated signs/symptoms: _____, _____, etc (give details). However, patient denied having_____, _____, etc (pertinent negatives). Patient received _____ (diagnosis, treatment) from the family doctor.

A few days before admission, patient developed_____, _____, (suicidality or homicidality) etc. and experienced _____, _____, etc. (stress, life changes, etc.) Subsequently, the_____(signs and symptoms) had become worse. Hence, a _____ (treatment - hospital admission or outpatient clinic) was sought.

This particular template includes the following core symptoms: symptomatology, stressors, chronology of symptoms/events, consequences of the problem, treatment received, pertinent negatives, and suicidality or homicidality

Example:

> *Ms. Y was apparently well until about three weeks ago when she developed depression after she found out that her best friend of many years committed suicide. She said that she was surprised that her friend did it since there was no apparent reason to do so. A week later, the patient became worse, this time her depression becoming associated with an inability to sleep, a lack of appetite, feelings of hopelessness, and thoughts of death.*

In this example, the statement Ms. Y was apparently well until describes the patient's usual clinical or normal state. Following closely is the time period about three weeks ago when the emotional difficulty began. These statements have established a clear-cut delineation between the normal and abnormal clinical status. Subsequently, you need to describe the chronology of significant events that need to be underscored in the history such as the worsening of the symptoms, inability to function, occurrence of thoughts of death, stressors, and treatment received. Attempt to relate the stressor to the worsening of symptoms. You may also describe the personal, psychosocial, familial, and occupational problems or distress related to the psychological signs and symptoms.

Example:

> *About a week prior to consultation, the patient reported her preference to stay at home, mostly in bed. She stopped going to the social club that she used to visit in the past. Her work began to suffer. Three days ago, her boss suggested that she needed to visit a psychiatrist in a nearby mental health clinic. After her first visit, the psychiatrist put her on Celexa for the depression and Desyrel for the sleep problem.*

Treatment received during crucial periods such as worsening of the patient's illness is noted. A major part of the presentation of HPI is the emphasis on pertinent negatives and the presence or absence of suicidality or homicidality. The reason for seeking help also needs to be established.

Example:

> *The patient got worse a week after the interview despite being on medication. She reported having thoughts of slashing her throat with a kitchen knife. However, she changed her mind after she thought of her kids. Now, she denies experiencing self-destructive thoughts and she contracts for safety. Moreover, the patient denied the presence of mania, psychosis or homicidality.*

Patients With Complicated Cases:

Sample template:
First Problem:

Mr./Mrs._____ is a___ year old male/female who has a long history of_____(psychiatric illness). Patient was apparently well until about _____ago when he/she started to experience_____(psychiatric symptom). The symptom was precipitated by _____ (stress, give details). _____ (duration) PTA, patient developed the following associated signs and symptoms: _____, _____, etc. Patient denied having_____, _____, etc. (*pertinent negatives). As a result of the above symptoms, the patient suffered impairment in functioning. Patient received _____ (diagnosis, treatment).

Second Problem:

Moreover, the patient reported having _____ (symptom) for the past _____ (duration). The symptom was associated with the following: _____, _____, etc. Patient denied having _____, _____, etc. (*pertinent negatives). Patient received _____, etc. (diagnosis/treatment).

On the day/few days prior to admission, the patient developed_____, _____, etc. and experienced _____ (stress, life changes, etc.) Hence _____ (treatment – admission, hospitalization) was sought.

*Pertinent negatives - give details

For patients with a complicated history, each problem deserves its own history and description. If, for example, your interviewee presents with both significant depression and OCD symptoms, then you have to explore both problems. Incorporate all information applicable to each problem. Always include the core components.

Example:

The patient was apparently well until about three months ago when she lost her job since she could not get along with her boss. She said that her boss was biased and that he was giving her a lot of unnecessary work. Subsequently, she developed anxiety attacks, occurring at least ten times a day. She described each episode as consisting of sudden occurrence of sweating, tremors of upper extremities, choking sensation, and palpitations lasting for about 10 minutes. About a month and a half later, she noticed that the symptoms got worse. She could not drive her car anymore, even to the grocery store. She developed a fear of going to work. Her functioning further deteriorated as she could no longer perform her usual daily chores, including making the bed and washing the dishes. Three weeks ago, she decided to visit a psychiatrist suggested by a friend. Since then she has been taking Prozac.

Furthermore, the patient had experienced mild depression for the past two years. She described the onset of depression as related to the death of her father with whom she was very close. For the past four weeks, she said that her depression got worse and that she was not motivated to do anything, even getting out of bed. Subsequently, her depression became associated with weight loss as she could not eat well. Her concentration was extremely impaired. However, she denied any presence of suicidal or homicidal ideation. She also denied the presence of psychosis, mania, and other symptoms.

Clinically Stable Patients But With Psychiatric History

Sample template:

Mr./Mrs. was apparently well until about _____ ago when patient developed _____ (psychiatric symptom). Such _____ (symptom) was precipitated by _____ (stress). Patient further reported the following: _____, _____, etc. (signs and symptoms). Mr./Mrs. _____ denied the following: _____, _____, etc. Patient received treatment such as _____, _____ etc. Subsequently, patient felt better and was discharged from the hospital.

As outpatient, patient was followed up by a mental health professional and underwent the following treatment: _____, _____, etc. Patient was _____ (compliant/noncompliant) with treatment.

Eventually, patient became clinically stable with no emotional difficulties.

Currently, patient reported feeling____. He participated in various activities such as ____, ____, etc. He remained ____(compliant/ noncompliant) with treatment regimens such as ____, ____, etc. (outpatient clinic, medication, etc.). He further denied any difficulties including suicidality or homicidality.

For stable patients with no current psychological symptoms or for those who are clinically stable but with a past psychiatric history, the presentation is approached differently. For these types of patients, it may not be appropriate to state the history of present illness since there is no present illness. It is better to present *history of mental illness* instead. This presentation, just like in the interview, includes the following: 1) previous psychiatric episode with its associated signs and symptoms, stressors, diagnosis and treatment, pertinent negatives, chronology, and so on, 2) subsequent events after the psychiatric episode such as outpatient treatment, 3) current functioning and status such as employment, support, and housing and, 4) current treatment. This technique affords a smooth flow from the past episode to current functioning with relative ease.

Example:

> *In terms of **history of mental illness**, Mr. W was apparently well until about five years ago when he experienced depression after his wife of 40 years left him for another man. He then felt extremely depressed for almost three months on a daily basis. He further reported that he had developed problems with his appetite and hence he had lost weight. He could not concentrate at his workplace so that, several weeks after the separation, he also lost his job. Subsequently, he remained in his bedroom the whole day due to feelings of weakness. His concerned neighbors convinced him to go to a hospital where he eventually*

stayed for approximately four weeks. He was put on SSRI which significantly helped him.

On discharge, he was followed up by the university psychiatrist almost twice a month initially, and then once per month. He also attended group and recreational therapies. Subsequently, his condition improved, with no associated emotional difficulties. He remained compliant with his treatment.

Currently, the patient reports feeling very good. He participates in various community and social activities. He remains compliant with medications, outpatient follow-up, and therapies. He further denies the presence of any significant emotional difficulties, including suicidality or homicidality.

But what if the past psychiatric episodes are so complicated that they include multiple hospitalizations and recurrent episodes? In such cases, you can choose a crucial event in the past, such as the last or most recent episode of mental illness, as the starting point of your presentation and then proceed to the current functioning and clinical status. Start with the announcement, *this is a patient with a long history of mental illness and psychiatric treatment who was his usual self until about . . .* Subsequently, you may describe in detail the last episode that resulted in hospitalization or in any form of treatment. Choosing the last episode of psychiatric illness is suggested because connection with the present is "easier." Other important information regarding the past psychiatric history, such as recurrences and suicidal or homicidal attempt, must be included.

Example:

*In terms of **history of mental illness**, the patient reported that he had a long history of mental   illness resulting in multiple hospitalizations and medication trial. He stated* *that about ten years ago, he began to think that the Russian mob was after him due to his connection with JFK. He told me that he could not hide from the mob since there was a telescope monitoring his every movement and there was a chip inside his teeth that guided the movement of the telescope. Moreover, he stated that he was also hearing the voice of Moses and Adam telling him that he was doomed to hell if he could not save the world from the clutches of the Mafia. Subsequently, he ended up in a mental institution after he was caught naked while directing traffic. He was put on a neuroleptic which gradually relieved his symptoms. After a few weeks, he was discharged to the community. At that time he was taking at least three medications.*

Subsequently, the patient significantly improved with the help of individual and group therapies. He attended the mental health clinic activities religiously, which included social skills and job training. His psychiatrist has seen him almost monthly for medication re-checks. He has remained stable clinically with enough support from his family and mental health staffs.

Currently, the patient states that he remains asymptomatic on current medications and therapy. He lives in his own apartment. With the help of the income he earns from part-time work, he is able to meet his basic needs. He denies having any emotional difficulties. He says that he is able to handle stress better this time. He denies having any suicidal or homicidal ideation for the past several months.

Other sample templates representing the remaining sections may be seen in the appendix section.

As in the interview, the use of mnemonic, outline, and checklist can be very powerful in organizing your presentation. Using the mnemonic SERIAL in presenting the patient's personal and social history, for instance, you simply cross out each letter in your mind after you finish presenting relevant information in that part of the history. This is a better method than randomly discussing the data you possess. You can also devise a checklist that includes must-know information or core components in each section of the history. During presentation, you state the information you checked off in your mind.

Just like in the interview, the oral presentation requires an outline. Establishing an outline representing the major sections of the psychiatric history may simplify the presentation process. You may organize your presentation based on the following accepted format:

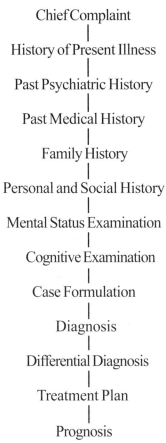

Chief Complaint
|
History of Present Illness
|
Past Psychiatric History
|
Past Medical History
|
Family History
|
Personal and Social History
|
Mental Status Examination
|
Cognitive Examination
|
Case Formulation
|
Diagnosis
|
Differential Diagnosis
|
Treatment Plan
|
Prognosis

Focus on one section until enough information is presented before moving to the next section.

The key, however, is establishing your own mnemonic, checklist, and outline that fits your style of interview and presentation. It should be easy to remember and user-friendly. You practice these organizing tools long before the exam, in your clinic and during mock reviews. A sample checklist can be found in the appendix.

𝑻𝑰𝑷𝑺

- Use templates, checklists, outlines, and mnemonics as effective organizing tools.

- Create organizing tools that contain the core components of each section and that fit your own interview style.

- The templates, checklists, outlines, and mnemonic should be user-friendly and easy to remember.

- Practice these organizing tools in your clinic and during mock reviews.

- Present *history of mental illness* for patients who are stable and with no current psychological signs and symptoms.

- For patients with a complicated psychiatric history, choose a crucial event in the past, such as the last episode of mental illness, as the starting point, and then proceed to the current functioning and clinical status.

CHAPTER 8

Powerful Case Formulation, Differential Diagnosis, And Treatment Plan

CASE FORMULATION

The case formulation is a summary of patients' emotional difficulties, history, predisposition to mental illness, and aggravating factors (Morrison and Munoz, 1996). It includes the following core components: current symptoms, brief past psychiatric history, precipitating or predisposing stressors, contributing factors, aggravating factors, safety issues, and other relevant issues to be addressed in treatment.

The case formulation signifies how well you understand the patient. Since it is only a summary, you should be brief. Although some literature espouses lengthy case formulation, with a strong emphasis on the psychodynamic mechanisms and themes, short and crisp formulation is the rule for the psychiatry oral exam. Psychodynamic themes may or may not be emphasized at length. Your comfort level is the gauge. If you think that you have a particular interest and good training in psychoanalysis or psychodynamic psychotherapy and that emphasizing it will help, you might decide to include psychodynamic considerations.

There are several acceptable ways of doing case formulation as shown by the examples below. First, you state the current symptoms, precipitating stressors, past psychiatric history, predisposing factors, contributing factors, safety issues, and other issues relevant to treatment.

Case formulation 1

Mr. W is a 56 y/o wm who has a prior history of major depressive disorder and psychiatric hospitalization. He was apparently well until his boyfriend of three years left him for another man. Subsequently, he developed depression with associated neurovegetative signs and symptoms, impairment in functioning, and severe distress. The patient reports a strong family history of depression on the mother's side. Other contributing factors include head trauma at age 17 due to a car accident. In addition, he has been abusing marijuana for the past two years.

In terms of safety, I do not think that the patient is a threat to himself or others at this time, as he denies any presence of self-destructive and violent thoughts. He also contracts for safety. Issues that need to be discussed in treatment include the patient's denial of his illness, and his need to practice safe sex.

Secondly, you include current symptoms, precipitating stressors, past psychiatric history, predisposing, contributing, perpetuating, or aggravating factors, defenses/adaptive style, safety issues, and other issues relevant to treatment.

Case formulation 2

This is Mr. W who experiences depressive signs and symptoms after his boyfriend left him. He reports prior treatment for depression. In terms of predisposing factor, the patient has a strong family history of depression on the mother's side. Other aggravating factors include the use of marijuana. His defensive style includes denial.

In terms of safety, I do not think that the patient is a threat to himself or others at this time, as he denies any presence of self-destructive and violent thoughts. He also contracts for safety. Issues that need to be discussed in treatment include the patient's denial of his illness, and his need to practice safe sex.

Thirdly, you include the following: current symptoms, precipitating stressors, past psychiatric history, biological, psychological, and psychosocial factors, safety issues, and other issues relevant to treatment.

Case formulation 3

Mr. W is 56 y/o who experiences depressive signs and symptoms after his boyfriend left him. He has a prior treatment for depression. Biologically, the patient has a strong family history of depression on the mother's side. He also uses marijuana daily. Psychologically, he had been sexually abused as a child. Psychosocially, he has lost emotional support from his family because of his alternative lifestyle.

In terms of safety, I do not think that the patient is a threat to himself or others at this time, as he denies any presence of self-destructive and violent thoughts. He also contracts for safety. Issues that need to be discussed in treatment include the patient's denial of his illness, and his need to practice safe sex.

DIFFERENTIAL DIAGNOSIS

The discussion and question-and-answer portion of the exam revolve around your major diagnosis. Make an appropriate diagnosis based on the information and materials you obtained from the thirty-minute interview and observation of the patient. However, it is not sufficient simply to make the diagnosis. It is imperative to support your diagnosis with evidence strong enough to meet the DSM IV criteria. Your diagnosis includes relevant rule outs. This is the best time to demonstrate your knowledge of the DSM IV and your mastery of the case.

For patients with multiple diagnoses, you have to first discuss the predominant illness that has contributed greatly to the patient's distress and functional dysfunction or the one with the most significant impact. Subsequently, talk about other major diagnostic considerations along with their supporting evidence.

I know some successful candidates who have practiced and prepared a predetermined differential diagnosis prior to the exam. They have written down all the possible causes of one major symptom and have memorized the differences pertaining to each disorder. In terms of depression, for example, they have differentiated major depressive disorder from dysthymic disorder, bipolar disorder, and depressive disorder due to medication, illicit drugs, alcohol or medical/neurological conditions. They have memorized the differential diagnoses and have practiced them in their minds, or in front of the mirror, several times prior to the examination. During the presentation in the oral exam, everything becomes "automatic." These candidates have told me that, after using this technique, they appear "flawless" before the examiners, since they do not have to wrestle for differentials and for appropriate words to articulate them.

If you decide to use this technique, make sure that your differentials and the supporting evidence conform to the data available. Consider a diagnosis as a differential only if the history and your MSE warrant it. You do not mention a diagnosis just for the sake of having one. Be aware that this technique has the disadvantage of relying heavily on rote memory. This process may make you vulnerable to anxiety, especially if the memorized data do not fit your patient's clinical information.

Moreover, know the most common medications, illicit drugs, medical or neurologic disorders that precipitate or cause a particular psychological symptom. If your patient has any of these conditions, such as hypothyroidism or stroke along with depression, it is easy to think of a differential diagnosis, especially if the board examiners insist on other diagnostic considerations.

Example:

> *In my opinion, the patient is suffering from major depressive disorder as evidenced by depression for a few months occurring on a daily basis, the presence of neurovegetative signs and symptoms such as lack of energy, inability to eat and sleep, impaired concentration, impairment in functioning, and distress.*

> *I would also consider the possibility of panic disorder because of the presence of intermittent panic attacks appearing suddenly and lasting for about ten minutes, associated with physical signs and symptoms such as sweating, tremors, palpitations, etc., and severe feelings of distress caused by the symptoms.*

> *It is worthwhile to consider the possibility of dysthymic disorder since the patient has mentioned being depressed for a while, but I do not have enough information to make a determination at this time.*

> *I would also consider the possibility of generalized anxiety disorder as evidenced by complaints of anxiety. However, at present this diagnosis is unlikely since the anxiety that*

he describes does not include worrying about other areas in his life. Moreover, his anxiety is not associated with restlessness, fatigue, impairments in concentration and sleep, muscle tension or irritability.

It is necessary to point out a key difference in presenting a live patient as opposed to dealing with one in the video. With regard to the live patient, the differential diagnosis should focus on one to three major diagnoses and one or two rule outs. A shotgun diagnosis, mentioning all the diagnoses in Kaplan and Sadock's comprehensive text, must be avoided because the board examiners may conclude that you are not sure of your diagnosis. In other words, one diagnosis with good supporting evidence is superior to a multiple diagnosis with insufficient evidence.

On the other hand, the differential diagnosis in the video part of the exam may involve all possibilities, even those supported only by clues or minimal data. In this context, several diagnoses may be given, at least two major diagnoses and several rule outs. In fact, the video part is actually intended for this purpose – to determine how well a candidate can explore possibilities based on limited information. I base this conclusion on the fact that the video is usually edited to the point where much vital information is intentionally not included. A function of the board examiners is to press you for more diagnoses during the video exam. But ultimately, you still need to single out the most probable diagnosis.

TREATMENT PLAN

The treatment plan should conform to the patient's diagnosis and level of severity, frequency, associated signs and symptoms, and disabling symptoms. For example, a female patient with mild depression associated with lack of sleep, occurring after a breakup with her boyfriend, may not warrant the use of anti-depressants. Individual needs, comfort level, insight, compliance and motivation to undergo treatment are included in the whole picture. Any hindrance to the effective implementation of the plan needs to be considered. Prior history and response to treatment also guide the choice. Prior family support for the plan can further strengthen the choice.

Moreover, the patient's capacity or incapacity to make treatment decisions may need to be established prior to making any recommendation. Board examiners may ask about it since treatment plan considerations may change depending upon the patient's decisional capacity. For example, a severely depressed individual with psychosis may not be considered capable of making treatment decisions. There may be a need to involve family members.

A referral to a specialist is considered only if there is enough information in the history and MSE that can strongly support such a request. A complaint of headache, for example, that comes after the start of medication may not warrant a neurological examination. But a headache described as chronic and progressive, associated with fainting and walking impairment, and that precedes psychological problems, may certainly warrant a neurology referral or perhaps a CT SCAN of the head. The request for a laboratory screen requires the same strong consideration of supporting data from the evaluation.

Organize your treatment plan in a clear and coherent manner. You may segregate your interventions into biological, psychological, or social interventions and discuss each one comprehensively. Alternatively, you need to mention the stages of treatment from emergency, or acute treatment to rehabilitative measures and long term care (Lowy and Prosen 1979). Kline and colleagues (1984) suggested dividing treatment intervention into immediate, short-term, and long-term management. In the same vein, APA treatment guidelines propose that clinicians provide acute therapy and eventually continuation and maintenance therapy. You may want to state the relevant biopsychosocial intervention in each stage of treatment.

Example 1:

In terms of treatment plan, I will approach this in a biopsychosocial manner.

Regarding biological intervention, I'll also do a physical examination to check for any organic pathology such as a neck mass that can cause the patient's current complaint. I will also order TSH to check for the presence of hypothyroidism as the cause of patient's psychomotor retardation and depression. I'll make appropriate referral to a specialist depending upon my findings. If the result of the examination and blood work is unremarkable, I'll start the patient on a SSRI 20 mg/day after discussion of its indication, side effects, risks and benefits, alternative treatment and prognosis with or without medication.

Psychologically, I'll provide individual psychotherapy that includes psychoeducation of patient's illness and medication, provision of support and reassurance, establishing therapeutic alliance, and discussion on cognitive and behavioral interventions to help the patient cope with the illness.

Socially, I'll meet with the family with the patient's consent to talk about issues such as housing, financial support, family education about patient's illness and medications.

Common biological, psychological, and social interventions are found below.

Biological intervention:

- Laboratory screens
- Referral to specialists
- Neuropsychological testing
- Rating scales

- Physical or a neurological exam
- Psychopharmacology
- Electroconvulsive therapy

Psychological intervention:

- Supportive psychotherapy
- Cognitive Behavioral Intervention
- Psychoeducation

> *Supportive Therapy* includes: support, education, therapeutic alliance, reassurance, support from family members, instilling hope, problem solving techniques, improving coping mechanisms, cognitive-behavioral intervention.

> *Cognitive intervention* includes: self-affirmation, identifying distortion, examining the evidence, double-standard method, experimental techniques, shades of gray thinking, cost/benefit analysis, reattribution, semantic techniques, definition of terms, survey method, so-what techniques.

> *Behavioral Intervention* includes: relaxation techniques, breathing exercises, progressive muscle relaxation, exercises, scheduling activity, diversion, socialization, recreational activities, hobbies, exposure.

Psychosocial Intervention:

- Increasing daily activities/skills
- Family education/sessions
- Housing
- Assertive techniques
- Conversational skills
- Job training

- Financing
- Socialization
- AA/NA

TIPS

- **Short and crisp formulation is the rule.**

- **Psychodynamic themes may or may not be emphasized in case formulation.**

- **Support your diagnosis with strong evidence.**

- **You may practice and prepare a predetermined differential diagnosis before the exam.**

- **Shotgun diagnosis must be avoided.**

- **The treatment plan should conform to patient's illness, level of severity anddisabling symptoms.**

- **Organize your treatment plan in a clear and coherent manner.**

CHAPTER 9

Practice And More Practice

After learning how to effectively organize your data, your next important activity is consistent practice. Practicing daily is the recommended strategy. The more practice you do, the more your presentation will appear spontaneous and routine. Daily mock review of your interview and presentation with a board certified psychiatrist is the most preferable. But this may not be practical since it is most difficult to find a colleague who could spare an hour of daily practice with you. Your colleagues have their own concerns and responsibilities. They may be willing to help but time constraints imposed by managed care, patient caseload, teaching and administrative functions, and family concerns certainly interfere with their enthusiasm to assist.

Even if some of your colleagues offer help, they will not be as motivated as you are. They might prefer to watch a replay of a championship boxing match, or follow special news stories. The situation is aggravated if you practice in a rural area, where the number of moose or caribou outnumbers the town's population. If you are the only psychiatrist in that area and if the next psychiatrist is about three hours away, how can you practice for the exam? An additional problem concerns finding a cooperative patient who is willing to undergo the same questions over and over again and who is accommodating enough to help "train" a psychiatrist.

I devised a few methods to compensate for the lack of access to practice and mock exams while I was preparing for my own oral exam last year. The methods allowed me to practice every day, and at anytime without bothering others, and they helped me realize that practicing by myself can be very gratifying and enlightening. I would like to share these techniques with you.

One method is to record your interview or presentation on a tape. You will be surprised with what you discover when you listen to yourself on a tape. Your accent, grammatical errors, and muddled thought process become more apparent. The second method is to record and watch yourself in a video, and look for grave errors in your interview and presentation. The third method is to watch yourself present a case in front of a mirror. In my opinion, these three techniques can substitute for the mock examination. Stepping outside yourself and closely watching your interview and presentation, demeanor, and style from a distance puts you in a more objective position to be a fact finder and faultfinder. However, to achieve success, you should not be lenient on yourself. Objectively assess yourself. Be your own harshest critic.

Core components:

- Tape-recording and video-taping interview or presentation
- Allowing a waiting period prior to the analysis
- Listening and looking for errors
- Planning to correct those errors
- Timing the presentation
- Repeating the process

I warn you that this process is not easy since it requires a lot of humility and self-discipline to accomplish the task successfully. This process requires a certain frame of mind, a positive and accepting attitude. Perhaps you wonder why certain character traits are needed in order to succeed in this endeavor. Well, it is a humbling experience to discover your mistakes yourself. Accepting criticism from others is far easier for some of us to take. For those who are chronically in denial and think that there is nothing wrong with them, any form of self-discovery prompts contempt and probably disbelief. I heard one colleague who, after seeing herself doing a disorganized interview in the video, quickly blurted out, "Oh it's not me. I can't believe it's me." Another colleague simply excused himself and stated that he was "sick" at the time after he saw himself in a video delivering a jumbled presentation.

It is challenging to discover one's mistakes. Rectifying them is a demanding task. Here self-discipline comes to the fore. The long hours necessary to do the job, the hard work of endless and repetitive taping and listening, the meticulous scrutiny of the interview and presentation for mistakes, the courage to step outside oneself, and the ability to accept a "lesser ego" – these all require both a positive and self-critical attitude.

RECORD YOUR INTERVIEW IN A TAPE

There are a number of steps to follow in recording one's interview or presentation on a tape and then criticizing it. First, adopt an attitude that enables you to identify your weaknesses without being lenient, placing in abeyance your strengths. Secondly, record your interview with a patient with the latter's written consent. Thirdly, record your presentation on tape immediately after seeing your clinic patient. It is better to record while all the information gathered is still fresh. Fourthly, allow a waiting period, probably at least six hours, before you actually listen to the tape. This waiting period gives you a useful distance from your presentation. Such distance is imperative for the sake of objectivity. It is also important that you are comfortable and well-rested when you listen to your tape. A longer waiting period, such as the next day, may be preferred. Fifthly, after the waiting period, begin listening to the tape and actively look for errors, even minor ones. Sixthly, establish a plan to correct those errors. Finally, practice at least once a day. The more practice, the better. Make sure that, in your next interview and presentation, you eliminate previous errors.

RECORD AND WATCH YOURSELF IN A VIDEO

A second mode of practice involves watching yourself in a video. This mode requires the same steps as the use of the tape but it may be more interesting since you see and hear yourself "live" doing an interview and presentation. This idea of using a self-video for the purpose of review came when I was preparing for the exam last year. I remembered that Dr. Land, a recognized expert on board exams, sent me free copies of the videotape of my mock exams with him. I reviewed those tapes repeatedly. The more I reviewed the tape, the more I realized my own mistakes, down to the most minute detail. Although I gained a lot of tips from Dr. Land, I learned much more from my analysis of my own performance. Subsequently, I learned how to prevent errors in my next presentations.

From this experience I concluded that, as a candidate for the oral exam, it is necessary to video tape at least one of your interviews and presentations so that you can see what needs to be avoided in actual exams. However, do not forget to ask for the patient's consent prior to any recordings of your interview. Again, be an objective self-critic. Look closely for disorganization, unclear speech pattern, inappropriate gestures, lack of eye contact, among others. Make a record of your mistakes and plan to correct them. Review the tape a few times until you see all possible errors.

Another strategy is having another psychiatrist view and criticize your video interview and presentation. Again, do not forget to ask for the patient's consent permitting others to review the tape. You may wish to conceal the identity of the patient in the video by blurring the face. Having a colleague view your video provides flexibility because it can be done at his/her convenience, minimizing conflict in your schedules. Furthermore, you can request other colleagues to view the tape in their own time and then comment on your performance. In this way you learn more about your errors and strengths.

WATCH YOURSELF PRESENT A CASE IN A MIRROR

Presenting a case in front of a mirror is the third method. When I did my review course, I attended several public interviews. I tried to recollect several patients' histories. Back at the hotel room, I positioned myself in front of a mirror and started to present. I did this several times until I felt comfortable with what I saw. I tried to notice any mannerisms or gestures that may be perceived as unnecessary and immature. I observed my facial expression for signs of aggression, anxiety and self-doubt. I scrutinized my voice for inflections that might indicate uncertainty. I made sure that my facie, voice, gestures, and speech were coordinated to deliver a passing result.

In summary, you certainly do not want to present too brief or too lengthy a history during the oral presentation. There is no hard and fast rule in making a presentation. But since this is an exam, then you should try to sound interesting. At least ten minutes may be spent for an easy, straightforward case, and approximately fifteen minutes for a complicated case. Try not to bore your examiners with lengthy and repetitive repertoire. Moreover, you should not give the examiners the impression that you are trying to avoid the question-and-answer-portion.

TIPS

- **Practicing daily is the recommended strategy.**

- **Prepare for the exam through mock reviews with a board certified psychiatrist.**

- **The more practice you do, the more your presentation will appear spontaneous and routine.**

- **Review your performance through the use of mirror, video, and tape and provide an objective self-criticism.**

- **In your next interview and presentation, try to eliminate prior errors.**

- **Allow another psychiatrist to view and criticize your video interview and presentation.**

- **It is challenging to admit one's mistakes. Rectifying them is a demanding test.**

PART III

ORGANIZE YOUR VIDEO EXAM

The video exam is unique and for some candidates it is more challenging than the live exam. In fact some candidates simply wilt under the pressure of taking this portion of the exam. They even question the reliability and validity of this process in evaluating their knowledge and clinical experience. There are many reasons why it is faced with dread and uncertainty. First, the video is intentionally edited, lacking important information that may be necessary in understanding the patient's whole picture. In fact some of the deleted information holds the key to a more accurate diagnosis, treatment plan, and prognosis. Secondly, the candidate has no control over the interview being watched. If your attention span is not great, you cannot turn around and ask the patient for any information you have missed. Anything you fail to get during the 25-minute period is gone forever. Thirdly, the video is an abnormal event in an abnormal environment. Our knowledge and clinical experience have developed from readings, supervision, and actual interviews with patients and not based on an analysis of an edited, and at times, poor quality video. Fourthly, many residency programs do not have a curriculum to prepare candidates for this process. They may have live interview and mock reviews but no specific training or mock review for the video part of the examination. Such a lack of emphasis probably results in lack of preparation and may have even created the impression among us that the video exam is not tough or important enough.

There are two basic strategies that I found helpful when I was preparing for the video examination: the stop, look and listen strategy and the note-taking strategy.

The Stop, Look, And Listen Strategy

The stop, look, and listen strategy reflects a commonsensical approach to video examination and it will help you negotiate the thorny environment associated with the video exam. You may think that this strategy is simplistic and of little use because it compares taking an exam to crossing the street. But taking the video exam is like crossing the street. When you cross a street, you wish to cross safely; you do not run unmindful of what might happen. Similarly, when you encounter the exam, you want to navigate safely by observing and being aware of the exam environment, so as to avoid "accident" and failure.

The *Stop* concept refers to the decision of the candidate to terminate any worries and rumination of prior or future events before taking the video examination. Tendencies to ruminate about unnecessary events, such as uncertainties in the recently concluded live interview exams or about personal and family problems, have to be eliminated. I once had a colleague who, after the live interview, became so consumed with the possible mistakes he committed that he could hardly concentrate on the video examination. He eventually failed to get any relevant information from the video. In another case, a friend of mine failed the video examination because she could not stop worrying about her family in Mozambique just a few hours before the exam. The first priority in the video exam is to practice the *stop* concept and focus on the task at hand. Any distractions should be put in your mental garage.

The *Look* concept refers to close observation of the patient in the video, to looking actively, not just watching. Here the candidate must be fully aware of the activities in the video environment. Try not to be distracted by noise, movements, or complaints created by other candidates in the exam room. If you are easily distracted by any of these external stimuli, consider sitting in front of the room close enough to the video. You have to concentrate fully on the video. Check for any unusual behavior, distinctive clothing or makeup, aberrant physique, abnormal movements, strange attitude, atypical speech inflections, peculiar affect, and cognitive impairment. In short, all observations may serve as clues to the possible psychiatric disorder. For example, a patient's response to internal stimuli may indicate psychosis, especially if pill-rolling tremors and bizarre affect are present.

The *Listen* concept refers to the active collection of information via listening. Make sure that the video sound is loud enough for you to understand. If you have trouble listening to the video, do not hesitate to inform the examiner about your concern as soon as possible. There is nothing to be gained by candidates who voice their complaints to colleagues and friends *after* the video exam.

Despite distractions, poor sound quality of the video, inadequate performance in the live interview, or editing in the tape, candidates should focus wholly on the task at hand.

TIPS

- **The stop, look, and listen strategy is a practical approach in negotiating the video exam.**

- **Terminate any worries and rumination of prior or future events before taking the video exam.**

- **Actively look for any pathology.**

- **Gather information through active listening.**

- **Focus on the task. Do not allow distractions to stop you from getting information.**

The Note-Taking Strategy

The note-taking strategy refers to making a written record of information gathered through the stop, look and listen strategy. This strategy serves several purposes.

The first purpose is to organize the information collected from the video into the different sections of psychiatric evaluation such as HPI, past psychiatric history, etc. Since the video clip shown in the exam is mostly edited and intentionally disorganized, it helps if you can organize the data in a coherent, sequential, and smooth fashion. The history of present illness information should not be mixed with that of the personal and social history or with that of the family history. Failure to organize the information may cause confusion to you and the examiners.

The second purpose of note-taking is to have something in written form for quick review prior to presentation. Most board examiners will give you one or two minutes to organize your thoughts. In my opinion, it is easier to organize your material if you have a written document that you can utilize for review. Quick review that relies on memory may be effective only if you have a photographic memory or if you are used to this type of mental routine. Otherwise, it is vital to have a text containing the information gathered.

The third purpose is to put in writing your initial impressions, provisional diagnoses or all possible differential diagnoses, and an initial treatment plan. As you know, the board certification examination is a highly charged and stressful event for most candidates. Such stress, along with anxiety and fear of failure, can precipitate a cascade of mental events that may result in mental lapses, confusion, and limited appreciation of the case presented in the video. It is certainly helpful if you write down some preliminary considerations, such as differential diagnoses, during the exam that can help refresh your understanding of the case in your presentation.

The fourth purpose of note-taking is to serve as a guide and as a memory aid during presentation. Your notes can serve as your peripheral memory, a wealth of information that you can retrieve, if necessary, during presentation. Your notes may help minimize mental lapses since you have information to review prior to the presentation and they refresh your memory during the presentation itself. However, you should not read the notes verbatim during presentation. I had seen review candidates who did exactly this, to the dismay of the mock reviewers. Unless you have a genius IQ level or a photographic memory, you will find this note-taking strategy generally beneficial.

Failure to take notes during the video examination is a common mistake I noticed in some candidates. Countless candidates told me that they paid a high price for not taking notes. There are a few effective techniques in note-taking. One is preparing the psychiatry evaluation template before the video examination. The template includes the entire sections essential in psychiatric evaluation, for example HPI, PMH, etc. A second technique, as the video progresses, is to fill out each section with the information you gather from the tape. An example is provided below. A third technique is to write down initial impressions, a provisional diagnosis, and even a treatment plan. A fourth technique is to write general points and to avoid writing detailed information. Remember though, you have to look closely at the video during the process.

Example:

Chief complaint

Anxiety

HPI

Anxiety -starts 3 months ago

grandmother passed away

can't sleep

feeling on edge

muscle tensed

used alcohol to calm nerves

Past Psychiatric History

had worries since childhood

no treatment

Past Medical History

unremarkable

Family History

"nerve problem" - cousin

use of illicit drugs - brother

Personal and Social History

single

no previous incarceration

finished computer engineering

MSE

Affect - anxious

psychomotor agitation

Differential Diagnosis

Generalized Anxiety Disorder
Adjustment Disorder
R/O Alcohol Abuse

Treatment Plan

Meds, psychotherapy, etc.

The same note-taking techniques can be applied during the live interview. A question arises as to the necessity and importance of taking notes in the interview. In my view, you may take notes only if you are used to this process for a significant while. If you regularly take notes in your training and clinical practice, it will not help if you suddenly change your style during the examination by not taking notes. Habits and behavior take months or years to learn and unlearn. Avoidance of taking notes, simply because the board review or mock examiner tells you so a few weeks before the exam, invites anxiety and confusion.

Know your comfort level and use your judgment in deciding whether to take notes. If you decide to take notes, make sure that the note-taking process does not interfere with the flow of the interview. Keep the notes brief and unobtrusive. Maintain frequent eye contact with the patient and infrequent eye contact with the notes. For those candidates who are not used to taking notes during regular clinic or mock interviews, my advice is **don't take notes** during the live interview. Again, last-minute changes in your interview style are unlikely to benefit you. They may, in fact, cause emotional turbulence since you are plunging into an unfamiliar territory at the wrong time.

TIPS

- **Note-taking helps in organizing and recording information.**

- **Your notes can serve as your peripheral memory, thus helping in quick review of data.**

- **Effective techniques in note-taking include writing the evaluation template prior to interview, filling out each section with gathered information, writing initial impressions and differential diagnosis, and writing only general points rather than details.**

- **Look closely at the video during the note-taking process.**

- **When note-taking during live interview, maintain frequent eye contact and keep your notes brief and unobtrusive.**

PART IV

DISORGANIZATION AND OTHER ISSUES

Disorganization during interview and presentation is not adventitious and is caused by a range of factors. Some of these factors including cognitive distortions, anxiety, and lack of preparation, are unfortunately self-induced. As such, they are not totally beyond your control. Practical interventions can be applied to reduce disorganization and contribute to exam success. Effective use of behavioral techniques, such as breathing exercises, compartmentalization, and so-what technique, minimizes negative expectations and emotion and lack of focus.

Moreover, negotiating impressively the question-and-answer portion of this exam cannot be left to chance. You need to know and practice helpful techniques to improve your performance in answering questions and in projecting a positive demeanor.

CHAPTER *12*

Dealing With Common
Causes Of Disorganization

ANXIETY

Anxiety is a common and understandable problem given that an important credential is at stake. The more the oral exam candidate experiences anxiety, the more it will have a negative impact on the candidate's performance. Such anxiety, whether warranted or not, can be caused by both rational and irrational factors. One of the most common irrational factors is the fear of failure. A lot of candidates have already visualized failure prior to and during the exam. This negative expectation has resulted in dismal performance. I know one candidate who simply had a mental block while taking the exam. He told me that he could not concentrate. His mouth was dry and his voice hoarse. He was sweating profusely and had experienced occasional tremors. In his mind, he was replaying so many *what ifs* – What if I fail? What would I do if the hospital knows that I fail? Will the

129

hospital kick me out? What will my friends say if I fail? After the exam, he almost knew the result since he could not answer questions made by the examiner. He also realized that he missed a lot of information during the interview because he did not concentrate.

This projection of failure should be minimized – in fact – replaced by positive thoughts such as the expectation of good performance and a passing result. Fear of failure should not be allowed to grow since it is a self-defeating exercise from which nothing can be gained. You have to remember that the board examiners will decide your fate, not you. The best you can do is help yourself pass the examination, not hurt your chances. Focus on the task at hand, such as establishing rapport with the interviewee, obtaining the core components of each section of the history and so on, rather than thinking about what might happen.

Some candidates have dealt with this problem well through the use of effective relaxation techniques. One technique is the use of deep breathing exercises prior to the actual interview. This involves the cycle of inhalation - holding your breath - exhalation - and holding your breath, while making a slow count to five during each phase. You may do this for five to ten minutes, especially prior to the interview. Another technique is a visualization of yourself for several minutes walking in a calm, beautiful, sunny environment such as a beach or a park. Try doing this along with the breathing exercise and you will be impressed with the result. Try other behavioral techniques such as progressive muscle relaxation when you prepare for the exam.

Some authors and clinical supervisors have suggested the trial of medications such as beta-blocker for severe performance anxiety. You may consider taking a beta-blocker only after you have tried it a few times before the actual examination and that based on this trial, you have not experienced any side effects or remarkable events such as dizziness and headache that impact negatively on your performance. Avoid benzodiazepines since this type of drug can cause memory lapses and sedation.

PREOCCUPATION WITH TRIFLES

Some candidates go to the examination well prepared for the task. They may have read textbooks and review books for three to four months prior to the exam. They may have done more than five mock exams with board certified supervisors. But when they go to the examination room, they seem to forget their mission of passing the exam. They become preoccupied with unnecessary thoughts and useless endeavors that cannot help them.

There are a number of cognitive distortions or trifles that candidates seem preoccupied with during the examination, making them unable to focus. One is the *missed opportunity* trifle. This refers to the tendency of the examinee to ruminate about anything he or she misses during the examination. Psychiatry exam candidates constantly recreate the questions they have failed to ask during the interview, questions they have failed to answer properly during the question-and-answer portion, and information they have failed to obtain during the interview. Candidates mentally replay these missed opportunities while the exam is still ongoing. As a result, they miss much information.

Secondly, there is the *I-should-have* or *I-could-have* trifle. This refers to the candidate's inclination to think about what ought to be or what ought to be done during the exam. It is typical for this type of examinee to think *I should have been given a helpful board examiner, I should have been provided with a cooperative patient not this difficult one, I could have done better if I read the Kaplan and Sadock's chapter on personality disorder,* etc.

Thirdly, we have the *fear-and-worry-of-the-possible-outcome* trifle. The candidate with this distortion simply cannot focus on the task at hand. The fear of failure seems to be more overwhelming than the examination itself. As a result of this fear, the candidate cannot concentrate, develops mental lapses, and experiences change in voice, posture, and style of interview.

As a psychiatrist attempting to become board certified, try to recognize the types of distortion that have prevented you from passing the examination. Do not be surprised if you have all of them. Having only one distortion will not make you a better passer. You have to recognize and if possible correct them before the exam. Try doing cognitive behavioral therapy on yourself before you fail again.

Some interventions can help. You may try focusing on the task at hand, focusing on the moment. Forget about the outcome because the outcome has never been predictable. Only the ABPN and the examiners will determine the result, not you. Do not worry about the possible errors of commission or omission. You can make mistakes but still pass the exam. You may develop an *I-don't-care* mental attitude regarding the outcome if you fear failure. This mental attitude is somewhat related to the *so-what* technique. Each time you feel the fear of failure, you can say to yourself: *So what! I can take the exam again.*

You may also try the compartmentalization technique. This simply refers to allocating your time to different tasks, thus avoiding any conflict. In this strategy, you tell yourself to focus first on the examination for one hour, and then allocate time to worry about anything else including the mistakes committed, five minutes after the exam. Each time you have the urge to worry, you tell yourself *I'll worry about this later.*

LACK OF CONFIDENCE

Some of us can easily be intimidated by the thought of taking the board certification exam. It is very daunting for many candidates to be doing the interview and presentation of the case in front of distinguished, board certified psychiatrists. It is not surprising that some candidates I spoke to had experienced difficulty organizing their thoughts in front of the examiners. Some have reported doing the interview well when placed in a clinical situation, such as the clinic or emergency room, but they seem to falter during the exam.

The best way to handle this problem is to practice rigorously. The more you are exposed to different interview situations, the more you are desensitized. The more mock exams you do with board certified clinicians, the better for you. Practice various techniques while interviewing your patients in the clinic, emergency room, or ward. After your interviews, do oral presentations in your office or at home. Do as many interviews and presentations as you can. If possible, record them in a tape or a video so you can criticize your own performance.

During the actual examination interview, try to forget the examiners' presence in the office. Think that you are doing the interview in your own clinic. In any case, do not forget to show enthusiasm and a positive attitude. Try to adjust your voice enough to project confidence and flair. Avoid postures and gestures such as stooping and scratching the head that project uncertainty.

LACK OF PREPARATION

A lot of candidates have underestimated the rigor of the exam, and their complacency works against serious preparation and study. Others have overestimated the exam's difficulty, finding themselves overwhelmed by the enormity of the task. In my view preparation is a must. I disagree with the common notion that you do not need to read about psychiatry simply because you have passed the written examination. Reading basic texts in psychiatry, psychopharmacology, and psychotherapy is needed to augment your knowledge. Devouring clinical practice guidelines can help in knowing the acceptable norm in assessment, interview, and treatment. Having an adequate knowledge is a big advantage in overcoming the difficulty of the question-and-answer portion.

Proper preparation that focuses on organizing skills and techniques discussed in the previous chapters need to be practiced frequently in any clinical situations prior to the examination. Organizing your interview and presentation is a daunting task that cannot simply be relegated to chance.

TIPS

- **Control your anxiety through cognitive and behavioral approaches.**

- **Do not be preoccupied with unnecessary thoughts and useless endeavors.**

- **Recognize and address your cognitive distortions.**

- **Frequent practice and exposure to different interview situations can help improve your confidence.**

- **Avoid gestures and postures that project uncertainty.**

- **Seriously prepare for the exam through constant study and by the application of organizing principles.**

Successful Negotiation Of
The Q & A Section

Organizing the question-and-answer portion is critical. Making an impressive start by organizing your interview, oral presentation, and video exam is winning only about two-thirds of the battle. You need to complete the race by making an impressive performance in the last part of the exam. This last phase is where your character and intelligence will be put to the test. This is the time that you will be grilled by board examiners who are investigating how well you know psychiatry and how well you understand your patient. This is an opportune time to show that your solid performance in the interview and presentation is not a fluke.

Several strategies should be employed to negotiate this part of the test. First, you need to focus on the task. Second, you have to prepare for any possible questions posed by the examiner. And third, you must present an appropriate demeanor.

FOCUS ON THE TASK AT HAND

The question-and-answer portion represents a task requiring your full concentration. Preoccupation with trifles as mentioned earlier, such as with your present and past personal or familial problems extraneous to the exam, is uncalled for. Worrying too much about your performance and possible failure in the interview and presentation thwarts your pursuit of diplomate status. Just focus and forget about the rest.

Give your full concentration to the questions. Be sure that you understand the questions the examiners are asking. If you do not completely comprehend a question, ask them politely to repeat it. It is better to ask than to give a correct answer to a different question. Ask the examiners to clarify or explain certain questions if you notice vagueness and ambiguity. Do not think that you appear foolish for doing so. In fact, the examiners may even think that you are careful when you do not rush your answers.

You have to decide early not to be distracted by any forms of noise, for example by the activities of the senior examiner. Do not feel intimidated by the occasional menacing style of some examiners. Although all examiners are instructed by the board to be "good and helpful" to the examinees, a few individuals' character flaws may unfortunately surface. Try to be patient since after a few minutes the examination is finished. Just give your best answer.

Try your best to accommodate questions that may seem irrelevant and off-tangent, or questions that represent unfamiliar territory for some recent graduates such as psychodynamic themes or psychoanalytic theories. Do not assume that your examiner will throw a "trick" question to keep you off-balance. In actuality, the majority of them are helpful and even give clues or "leads" towards a successful answer. In general, answer all questions politely even if the process of questioning interrupts you from your "flawless" presentation. Do not be bothered by them. Keep your focus.

PREPARE FOR ANY POSSIBLE QUESTIONS

As I outlined in my book Passing Strategies, there are three types of questions that you may be asked during the psychiatry oral exam: 1) questions based on the history and mental status examination (MSE), 2) questions based on your answers to prior question, and 3) hypothetical questions. In that book, I listed some possible questions that may be asked by board examiners to assess your knowledge, level of preparation, and understanding of your patient.

For the first type, questions based on history and MSE, make sure that your answer can be supported by facts as actually shown in the history and MSE. If, for example, the board examiner asks for your diagnosis, then you have to state the symptoms and signs, relevant history and observations obtained from the patient that support the diagnosis. There is no need to exaggerate or add information not found in the patient. Fabricating information is disastrous to your credibility and your chance of passing.

Moreover, make sure that you have a rationale for all your answers. If the examiners ask you about appropriate laboratory tests, you do not order tests "left and right" for the sake of having them. You must have a justification for every test you order. For example, if you think CBC is necessary, do not say that you are ordering it because this was your practice in residency. Your justification for ordering it, such as to establish a baseline, to rule out anemia that can cause depression, or to check the possibility of abnormality secondary to the use of mood stabilizers, needs to be clearly stated.

In dealing with the second type, questions based on answers to prior questions, you have to be mindful of anything that you articulate. Anything you mention can be a focus of further interrogation. If you mention a type of defense mechanism or a psychoanalytic theme, the board examiners will not hesitate to grill you on this subject. The important message here is to never mention anything you are unfamiliar with or something you cannot properly justify. It is safer to direct your energies to your area of expertise.

The third type, hypothetical questions, may pose a big challenge since this is the type of questioning that is totally out of your control. As you well know, the examiners may ask any questions under the sun and some of them may open the door to the unfamiliar. As a result, this type of questioning is anxiety provoking to a lot of candidates. The only effective way to deal with this is through sufficient preparation. In the book Passing Strategies, I advocated a method of preparation that involves reading if not mastery of at least one basic text and clinical practice guidelines. One reason for this suggestion is the possibility of hypothetical questions during the exam. How can you sufficiently understand *neuroleptic malignant syndrome* and its management without adequate study? How can you define *tardive dyskinesia* or treat refractory depression without reading basic texts? This is why I strongly disagree with some review courses which recommend not reading basic texts in preparation for the oral exam. They assume that, because you have already passed the written exam, reading basic texts is unnecessary at this later stage. The assumption is unwarranted.

In general, you need to prepare for any type of question. Ask your colleagues at work, clinical supervisors, and co-residents who have previous psychiatry oral exam experience for common questions asked. Alternatively, you may need to anticipate any questions that may be asked about a particular disorder, investigation, or treatment intervention. For example, for a patient with major depressive disorder, you may be asked about its differential diagnosis, possible etiologies, laboratory exams to be entertained to rule out medical conditions, and common medications. For a patient diagnosed with bipolar disorder and on mood stabilizers, you may be asked about the blood exams necessary to establish a baseline and its frequency, possible side effects and so on.

Another technique you can try is to master a predetermined answer to common questions long before the exam. This strategy is applicable to almost any subject including differential diagnosis, DSM IV criteria, etiologies, drug of choice and treatment strategies for refractory conditions, and definitions of pathological situations such as tardive dyskinesia, delirium tremens, serotonin syndrome, neuroleptic malignant syndrome, and priapism.

ORGANIZE YOUR ANSWERS

Kline and Fleming (1989) emphasize the need to organize your answers to questions. They further stated that in answering questions on treatment regimen, it is important to organize your recommendation from an immediate, short-term, and long-term standpoint. Presenting a correct answer is not sufficient in itself. You have to present your answer in a simple, coherent and logical way. Your answers should be given in a straightforward and forthcoming manner (Holden, 1991).

Make sure that your answers are based on sufficient evidence. James (1966) suggests that your answer is better when it begins with main points followed by supporting statements. For instance, if you are asked about your diagnosis of schizophrenia, you have to state all the facts present in the history, MSE, and physical exam which support your diagnosis. The example below illustrates this point.

> *In my opinion the patient is most probably suffering from schizophrenia as evidenced by the presence of auditory hallucinations, bizarre delusions, and progressive deterioration of functioning for the past six months. The patient manifests a blunted affect, disheveled appearance, and response to internal stimuli during evaluation. The diagnosis is further strengthened by a strong family history of schizophrenia from both sides.*

SHOW AN APPROPRIATE DEMEANOR

You should realize that the question-and-answer portion of the exam is also an exercise in humility. Here your character is put on

139

trial. Although it is always appropriate to demonstrate your intellectual prowess before the examiners, do not pretend to be an all-knowing psychiatrist ready to conquer the ABPN world. If you do not really know the answer, say so. Honesty is a virtue. Claiming that you know the answer very well, when in fact you know it only superficially, will not stand you in good stead.

There is nothing wrong in admitting issues you left out of the interview, things you would want to know if you had more time. It is likewise appropriate to admit limitations in your knowledge about a particular subject, for instance the management of anticholinergic crisis. The examiners understand that not everyone can be an expert on some rare pathological conditions. Nevertheless, you should convey to the examiner how you intend to gain knowledge and experience about the matter in question. Thus you may follow up your I-don't-know statements with pronouncements indicating your intention and willingness to get help from others, such as *I'll look it up, I'll consult my colleague*, and so on. An example is shown below.

How are you going to treat anticholinergic crisis?

Aside from stopping the drugs involved, I don't know exactly how to approach the problem. But I'm going to look up the literature about the current treatment intervention while immediately calling for internal medicine consultation.

Or you may answer it somewhat differently as shown below:

I'm sorry, I don't know how to go about it in detail. I will monitor the clinical status closely and I will seek the immediate help of my clinical supervisor who has significant experience and knowledge about drug side effects. I will also seek an immediate internist consultation. Meanwhile, I'll try to get as much information about the condition myself.

In negotiating the question-and-answer portion, display your confidence throughout despite the difficult questions you must face. Try to appear calm and collected all the time despite an occasional feeling of intimidation. Always be respectful to your examiners. Be patient. After all, you're nearing the end of the exam!

Remain focused to the end and maintain good eye contact with the board examiners in giving an answer. Reduce your uncertainty by focusing on the questions posed by the examiners and by polishing your answers. Most importantly, appreciate the uniqueness of this encounter. This may be your last chance to interact with these examiners.

TIPS

- Give your full concentration when tackling the question-and-answer portion.

- Ask the examiners to clarify or explain certain questions if you notice vagueness and ambiguity.

- Make sure that you have a good rationale for all your answers.

- Anticipate any questions that may be asked about a particular disorder, investigation, or treatment intervention.

- Master a predetermined answer to common questions long before the exam.

- Present your answer in a simple, coherent and logical mode.

- Learn how to say *I don't know* if you really do not know the answer.

- Follow up your I-don't-know answer with pronouncements showing your intention and willingness to get help from others.

CONCLUSION

The road to success in the psychiatry oral exam consists of a long, complex, and uphill course. It is not meant to be effortless since the purpose of the exam is to assess whether the examinee has the necessary skills and traits needed to provide treatment to the mentally ill and to offer comfort to the needy. The assessment process itself is not perfect, and as such, is not devoid of debate, ambiguity, subjectivity and occasionally contempt.

I lament the fact that there is no recognized formula for successfully facing this hurdle. Preparatory courses mostly lack uniformity in focus and methodology. This book has attempted to describe and discuss some practical techniques and strategies to improve your chances of passing the exam. I hope that this treatise has provided some basic knowledge in organizing your interview and oral presentation. I trust that some of the crucial interventions discussed to cope with the causative factors resulting in disorganization may help you execute an acceptable and passing performance.

As the saying goes, crisis is an opportunity to make better of yourself. In my view, the board certification exam, considered by many as an obstacle, prepares you for life's difficult and continuing climb to the top.

APPENDICES

A. CHECKLIST

Identifying Data:
Name: **Age:**   **Sex:**
Marital Status:
Inpatient or Outpatient:

Chief Ccomplaint:

History Of Present Illness(HPI):

__Depression __Anxiety __Hallucinations/delusions
__Panic attacks __Elevated mood __Irritability __Intoxication
__Memory loss __Withdrawal signs/symptoms __Mood swings
__Violence/aggression __Intrusive thoughts/compulsive behavior
__Alcohol/illicit drug use __Abnormal eating pattern __Others

Duration: __Years__Months __Weeks __Days __Hours
Frequency: __Daily __Weekly __Monthly
              __Constant __Frequent __Occasional __Rare

Associated Signs and Symptoms:

__Insomnia/hypersomnia __Appetite loss/increase __Psychosis
__Poor energy/ hyper energy__Lack/lots of interest__Distress
__Impaired concentration __Slow thinking/mobility
__Suicidality/homicidality   __Restlessness/agitation
__Guilt feelings__Physical signs and symptoms__Impairment in
   personal, social, academic and occupational functioning
__Hopelessness, helplessness, worthlessness __Mood problems
__Thoughts of death __Others

145

Stressors:
Current Treatment/medications:
Coping Mechanisms:

HPI (Details):

Past Psychiatric History:

__Unremarkable/denied/unknown __Mental illness __Duration

Details:
__Treatment Details: __Hospitalization Details:

__Suicidal ideation/attempt __Homicidality __Violence/
                                                    aggression
Details:(method, frequency, etc.)

__Use of alcohol/illicit drugs   Details:
__Detox/rehab __Out/inpatient treatment __Withdrawal signs
                                                and symptoms
__AA, NA, etc. __Legal problems __Impairment in
                                        functioning/relationships
__Sexual, physical, emotional, verbal abuse   Details:
__Traumatic experience   Details:

Past Medical History:

__Unremarkable/denied/unknown __Head injury/trauma
__Thyroid disease__Neurologic disorder __Pregnancy
__Allergy __Others:
__Medications   Details:

Family History:

__Unremarkable/denied/unknown __Mental illness
__Treatment __Hospitalization Details:

__Suicidality/homicidality   ___Violence/aggression
__Details:

__Alcohol/illicit drug use   Details:

Personal And Social History:

__Education __Employment __Relationships
__Legal record (includes current litigation)

Details:

Mental Status Examination:

Appearance	**Attitude**	**Behavior**
__Appropriate	__Friendly	__Normal
__Unkempt	__Cooperative	__Agitation
__Disheveled	__Hostile	__Retardation
__Others:	__Others:	__Others:

Abnormal Movements	**Eye contact**
__Slow	__Good
__Tremors	__Fair
__Cogwheel rigidity	__Poor
__Others:	

Speech	**Affect**	**Mood**
__Clear, goal-directed	__Neutral	__Euthymic
__Abnormal	__Depressed	__Depressed
__Rate	__Anxious	__Anxious
__Rhythm	__Angry	__Elevated
__Volume	__Irritable	__Others:
__Presence of defect	__Inappropriate	__Others:
__Constricted	__Blunted/flat	__Others:

Thought process	**Thought Content**
__Appropriate	__Appropriate
__Tangential	__Hallucinations
__Looseness of association	__Delusions
__Flight of ideas	__Overvalued ideas
__Circumstantial	__Paranoia/suspiciousness
__Impoverished	__Obsessions/phobias
__Thought-blocking	__Others
__Others	

Suicidality
__Denied
__Ideation
__Attempt
__Plan
__Intention

Homicidality
__Denied
__Ideation
__Attempt
__Plan
__Intention

Details:

Judgment
__Good
__Fair
__Poor

Insight
__Good
__Fair
__Poor

Cognitive Examination:

__Generally intact   __Aphasia   __Apraxia
__Agnosia   __Memory impairment
                  __Immediate __Recent __ Long-term
__Impairment in concentration/attention   __Disorientation
                                                      __Place
__Abstract reasoning impairment   __Time
                                                      __Person
Details:

NOTE: In this section, you may inquire about topics or areas that you are not able to ask in the previous sections, such as presence of compulsion, obsession, psychosis, mania, abnormal movements, agitation, and cognition.

B. TEMPLATES

HISTORY OF PRESENT ILLNESS

1) Simple Case

Mr./Mrs/Ms __is a __year old male/female who was apparently well until about __ ago (duration) when he/she started to experience__(symptom). Such __(symptom) was precipitated by___ (stress - give detail). ___(duration) PTA, patient developed the following associated signs/symptoms: ___,___, etc. However, patient denied having___, ___, etc. Patient received ___ (diagnosis, treatment).

Few days before admission, patient developed__, __(suicidality or homicidality) etc. and experienced ___, ___, etc. (stress, life changes, etc.) Hence the admission.

2) Patients With Complicated Cases

First Problem:

Mr./Mrs.__ is a __year old male/female who has a long history of ___ (psychiatric illness). Patient was apparently well until about ___ago when he started to experience ___(psychiatric symptom). The symptom was precipitated by ___ (stress, give detail). ___(duration) PTA, patient developed the following associated signs and symptoms: ___, ___, etc. Patient denied having ___, ___, etc. (pertinent negatives). As a result of the above symptoms, the patient suffered impairment in functioning. Patient received ___ (diagnosis, treatment).

Second Problem:

Moreover, the patient reported having ___ (symptom) for the past ___(duration). The symptom was associated with the following: ___, __, etc. Patient denied having ___, ___, etc. (pertinent negatives). Patient received diagnosis/treatment ___, etc. On the day/few days prior to admission, the patient developed ___, ___, etc. and experienced __ (stress, life changes, etc.) Hence the admission.

Pertinent negatives - give details

3. Clinically Stable Patients But With Psychiatric History

Mr./Mrs. was apparently well until about __ago when patient developed __(psychiatric symptom). Such __(symptom) was precipitated by ___(stress). Patient further reported the following: ___, ___, etc. (signs and symptoms). Mr./Mrs. ___ denied the following: ___, ___, (pertinent negatives) etc. Patient received treatment such as ___, ___ etc. Subsequently, patient felt better and was discharged from the hospital.

As outpatient, patient was followed by a mental health professional and underwent the following treatment: ___, ___, etc. Patient was ___(compliant/noncompliant) with treatment. Eventually, patient became clinically stable with no emotional difficulties.

Currently, patient reported feeling ___. He had participated in various activities such as ___, ___, etc. He remained __(compliant/ noncompliant) with treatment regimens such as ___, ___,etc.(outpatient clinic, medication, etc.). He further denied any difficulties including suicidality or homicidality.

DIFFERENTIAL DIAGNOSIS

In my opinion, the patient is suffering from ___(provisional diagnosis) as evidenced by: ___, ___, etc. (supporting evidence). I would also consider the possibility of ___ (diagnosis) because of the presence of ___, ___, (signs and symptoms) etc. It's worthwhile to consider ___ (diagnosis) due to the presence of ___, ___, (signs and symptoms) etc. But it is unlikely because of the following: ___, ___, (pertinent negatives) etc.

CASE FORMULATION

TEMPLATE 1

This is Mr./Ms. ___ who experiences ___(signs and symptoms) after___ (Stressor). Patient has a history of ___(past psychiatric history) and treatment ___. Patient has a strong family history of ___(psychiatric illness) which could have predisposed him/her to experience ___(major symptom). Other contributing factors include: ___, ___, etc. (medical problems, alcohol and drug abuse, physical and sexual abuse, etc.)

In terms of safety, I would say that patient is a ___ (threat / not threat) to self or others because of ___, ___, etc. There are further issues that need to be addressed in treatment: ___, ___, etc.

TEMPLATE 2

This is Mr./Ms. ___who experiences ___(signs and symptoms) after ___ (stressor). Patient has a history of ___(past psychiatric history) and treatment ___. In terms of predisposing factors, patient ___ (family history, mental retardation, etc.). Other aggravating factors include: ___, ___, (chronic stressors, etc.) Patient's defenses or adaptive style is characterized by: ___, ___, etc.

In terms of safety, I would say that patient is a ___(threat/ not threat) to self or others because of ___, ___, etc. There are further issues that need to be addressed in treatment: ____, ___, etc.

TEMPLATE 3

This is Mr./Ms. ___who experiences ___(signs and symptoms) after ___ (stressor). Patient has a history of ___(past psychiatric history) and treatment ___. Biologically, patient has ___ (medical problems, drug abuse, etc.). Psychologically, patient reports ____, ____, etc. (sexual abuse, distant mother, etc.). Psychosocially, patient has ____, ___, etc.(ongoing stressors, lack of support, etc.).

In terms of safety, I would say that patient is a ___(threat/ not threat) to self or others because of ___, ___, etc. There are further issues that need to be addressed in treatment: ____, ____, etc.

REFERENCES

American Psychiatric Association. Practice Guidelines. Washington, D.C.: APA; 1996.

American Psychiatric Association. Practice Guidelines for the Treatment of Patients with Schizophrenia. Washington, D.C.: APA; 1996.

American Psychiatric Association. Diagnostic and Statistical Manual of Mental Disorders. 4th ed. Washington, D.C.: American Psychiatric Association; 1994.

First MB, Frances A, Pincus HA. DSM IV Handbook of Differential Diagnosis. Washington, D.C.: American Psychiatric Press, Inc.; 1995.

Holden NL. MRCPsych Part Two: the oral examination. Brit J Hosp Med1991 Aug; 46(2): 120-21.

James DE. Answering examination questions. Nurs Times 1966 Mar;62(11): 385-6.

Kline S, Fleming S, Warme G. Passing the oral examination for specialist qualification in psychiatry. Can J. Psychiatry 1984 Apr; 29(3): 269-74.

Lane J, Lange E. Writing clearly: an editing guide. 2nd ed. Boston: Heinle and Heinle; 1999.

Lowy FH, Prosen H. The Canadian certification examination in psychiatry III: towards better certification techniques. Can J Psychiatry 1979; 24(4): 292-301.

Morrison J. The First Interview: Revised for DSM IV. New York: The Guilford Press; 1995.

Morrison J, Munoz RA. Boarding Time. 2nd ed. Washington, D.C.: American Psychiatric Press, Inc.; 1996.

Rayel MG. Passing Strategies: A helpful guide for the psychiatry oral exam. Newfoundland: Soar Dime; 2000.

Robinson DJ. Mnemonics and More for Psychiatry. 3rd ed. Port Huron, Michigan: Rapid Psychler Press; 2001.

Shea SC. The delicate art of the initial interview: traps, roadblocks, strategies, and solutions. Lecture presented at the 3rd Annual McMaster Muskoka Seminars; 1999 Jul 05-09; Huntsville ON.

SUGGESTED READING/VIEWING MATERIALS

Frances A, Ross R. DSM IV Case Studies: A Clinical Guide to Differential Diagnosis. Washington, D.C.: American Psychiatric Press, Inc.; 1996.

Gelula MH. Preparing and organizing for a lecture. Surg Neurol 1997; 47:86-8.

Gelula MH. Effective lecture presentation skills. Surg Neurol 1997; 47:201-4.

Hyman SE, Arana GW, Rosenbaum JF. Handbook of Psychiatric Drug Therapy. 3rd ed. Boston: Little, Brown and Co; 1995.

Stern TA, Herman JB, Slavin PL, Editors. The MGH Guide to Psychiatry in Primary Care. New York: Mc-Graw Hill; 1998.

Hall DP. 200 Tips for Passing the Oral Psychiatry Boards: Meeting the ABPN Challenge. Philadelphia, PA: Hanley & Belfus, Inc.; 1997.

Holden N. Clinical exams: interviewing in front of examiners. Brit J Hosp Med 1992 Sep 2-15; 48(5) 259-60.

Jongsma AE, Peterson LM. The Complete Psychotherapy Treatment Planner. New York: John Wiley and Sons, Inc.; 1995.

Kaplan HI, Sadock BJ. Synopsis of Psychiatry. 8th ed. Maryland: Williams and Wilkins; 1998.

Kline S, Fleming S. Passing the oral examination for specialist qualification in psychiatry: part II. Can J. Psychiatry 1989 Dec; 34(9): 925-26.

Lancaster J. Public speaking can be improved. The Journal of Nursing Administration 1985: 31-35.

Land WB. Strategies for Passing the Oral Boards Vol. 10[video recording] MA; 1998.

Land WB. Strategies for Passing the Oral Boards Vol 9[video recording] MA; 1998.

Land WB. Strategies for Passing the Oral Boards Vol 1[video recording] MA; 1997.

Leichner P, Sisler GC, Harper D. A study of the reliability of the clinical oral examination in psychiatry. Can J. Psychiatry 1984 Aug; 29(5): 394-97.

Lowy F, Dongier M. The Canadian certification examination in psychiatry II: who passes and who fails. Can J Psychiatry 1977; 24(4): 284-92.

Maxmen JS, Ward WG. Psychotropic Drugs Fast Facts. 2nd ed. New York: W.W. Nortion and Co.; 1995.

McConville B. Hints on passing post-graduate clinical and oral examinations in psychiatry. Aust N Z J Psychiatry 1982 Jun; 16(2): 73-8.

McCormick WO. A practice oral examination rating scale-inter-observer reliability. Can J. Psychiatry 1981 Jun; 26:236-39.

McDermott JF, Tanguay PE, Scheiber SC, Juul D, Shore JH, Tucker GJ et. al. Reliability of the part II board certification examination in psychiatry: examination stability. Am J Psychiatry 1993 Jul; 150(7): 1077-80.

Morgenstern AL. A systematic approach for oral board examinations in psychiatry. Amer. J. Psychiat. 1972 Jul; 129(1): 54-8.

Novales PN, Rojcewicz SJ, Peeles R. Clinical Manual of Supportive Psychotherapy. Washington D.C.: American Psychiatric Press, Inc.; 1993.

Pascal GR. The Practical Art of Diagnostic Interviewing. Homewood, Illinois: Dow Jones- Irwin; 1983.

Pokorny AD, Frazier SH Jr. An evaluation of oral examinations. J of Med Educ 1966 Jan; 41(1): 28-40.

Rudy LH, Kulieke MJ. Reasons given for success after initial failure on the American board of psychiatry and neurology part II examination. Am J Psychiatry 1981 Dec; 138(12): 1612-15.

Shea SC. Psychiatric Interviewing: The Art of Understanding. 2nd ed. Philadelphia, PA: WB Saunders; 1998.

Spinler SA. How to prepare and deliver pharmacy presentations. AJHP 1991 Aug; 48:1730-38.

Thomas C, Mellsop G, Callender K, Crawshaw P, Ellis P, Hall A et. al. The oral examination: a study of academic and non-academic factors. Medical Education 1992; 27: 433-39.

Thompson WM, Mitchell RL, Halvorsen RA, Foster WL Jr, Roberts L. Scientific presentations: what to do and what not to do. Invest Radiol 1987; 22:244-45.
Tohen M, Frankenburg FR. Preparation for the certification examination. Can J. Psychiatry 1983 Oct; 28(6): 471-4.

Trigwell P, Williams C, Yeomans D. MRCPsych examination technique: presenting to the examiners. Br J Hosp Med 1996; 56(6): 27

INDEX

Passing Strategies: *A Helpful Guide for the Psychiatry Oral Exam* is a practical approach to dealing with the complexities of the psychiatry oral exam. Dr. Michael Rayel combines fact and humor, personal vignettes and the experience of others to demonstrate effective methods for successful exam preparation and performance. **Passing Strategies**, with its many tips and solid advice will help allay the dread and exasperation confronting oral exam candidates.

"Michael Rayel, M.D. has written a textbook, guidebook, and workbook, all in one, designed to overcome those oral board anxieties by application of the old principle, 'knowledge is power.' But knowledge about psychiatry itself would not be enough to take on the oral boards. Instead, Dr. Rayel draws on personal, peer, and literature-based experience to provide practical strategies for both preparation for and participation in the oral board examination.

. . .This is an extremely user-friendly guidebook, which candidates will read and reread as the magic date draws closer. The no-nonsense suggestions are clear and basic and the underlying rationales eminently sound. Beyond those points, the moral support provided by the text is extremely solid."

Excerpt from the FOREWORD by: Thomas G. Gutheil, M.D.
                                        Professor of Psychiatry
                                        Harvard Medical School

ISBN: 0-9687816-0-8
Price: $24.95 (Paperback)   #Pages: 87
With CD and cassette version
Company's Name: Soar Dime Limited
  Phone: 709-466-5114
  Fax: 709-466-2214
  Website: www.soardime.com
  E-mail: info@soardime.com

For individual Orders: Call **1-866-41U-PASS** (1-866-418-7277)

For bulk orders/wholesalers/retailers, contact our distributor:
  Independent Publishers Group **- 1-800-888-4741**